# Kids SPEAK 7

## chaim walder

**Translated by Aviva Rappaport**
**Illustrated by Devorah Benedict**

FELDHEIM PUBLISHERS

Originally published in 2013 in Hebrew as
*Yeladim Mesaprim al Atzmam* (Vol. 7)

First published 2013
ISBN 978-1-59826-973-4

Copyright © 2013 by
Chaim Walder

Edited by Suri Brand
Typeset by LG Studios

FELDHEIM PUBLISHERS
POB 43163 / Jerusalem, Israel

208 Airport Executive Park
Nanuet, NY 10954

www.feldheim.com

10 9 8 7 6 5 4 3 2 1

*Printed in Israel*

To my precious children
Tzviki and his wife Yafi,
Moishe, Dudi, Noa, Tovi, Tali, and Racheli,
and to my grandson, Itamar

# Contents

# Preface

To parents (and kids who understand)...

Twenty years ago, I published *Kids Speak 1*. At the time, I was a young teacher who thought to reach his students' hearts by writing about their feelings.

In that first book, I included an address, POB 211, Bnei Brak, Israel, and invited children everywhere to express their feelings and tell me about themselves. In my wildest dreams, I never imagined the tremendous response that book would get.

Now it's obvious that *Kids Speak* is not just another series, but a way of life that encourages children to get in touch with their feelings and express them instead of ignoring them.

*Kids Speak* stories can be divided into three categories:

1. **Stories that evoke a response.** These stories help children (and—surprise!—adults as well) remember

similar situations that happened to them. They may have suppressed the memory, they may feel ashamed about what happened, or they might not have known how to talk about it. When someone else tells a story about a similar incident, they can allow themselves to talk about it as well.

2. **Adventure stories.** In these stories, the child is the hero. He acts courageously when appropriate and refrains from acting in ways that are physically, socially, or spiritually dangerous for him.

3. **Stories with a moral.** These stories touch the soul of both child and adult, reaching places deeply hidden from view—places where past insults, hurts, and guilt feelings linger. These stories soothe the pain, facilitate the healing process, and sometimes even heal the wounds completely.

The children who read *Kids Speak* when it first appeared, and grew up with *Kids Speak* stories as part of their lives, are now parents themselves. Twenty years is a good gauge of how important it is for children to see feelings written about, how crucial it is to encourage and legitimize the expression of feelings, and how vital it is to give sensitive guidance to each and every child on how to act in a wide range of personal, emotional, social, learning, and family situations.

Many years have passed since that first *Kids Speak* was published. Since then I have published other series: after *Kids Speak* came *Real Kids* and *People Speak* plus numerous other books for preschool readers, children, teens, and adults, all of them speaking to the vast and amazing world called "the soul of man."

During that time, I also became an educational consultant and have the privilege of being a founder and the director of the Child and Family Center in Bnei Brak, where most of my work takes place. My daily interactions with children (and parents) keep me—and my writing—in touch with today's children and youth.

I wrote *Kids Speak 1* as a young father of an eighteen-month-old. Now, twenty years later, I'm a grandfather of an eighteen-month-old. But I still feel young, sometimes even like a child, thanks to my work with children and my books for them.

It gives me great pleasure to bring you *Kids Speak 7*, the seventh book in the series that means so much to me.

With deep appreciation to the Creator of the world for all He has given me in the past...and with a prayer for the future.

Because it's all from Him.

Chaim Walder

# Police Panic

**My name is Ari.**

I'm ten and a half, and I live in Netivot.

I'm a happy, popular kid, maybe a little bit mischievous, but not wild. Last year, if you'd have asked my friends if I was a scaredy-cat, they would've told you, "No, not at all—except for…"

The "except for" referred to something of which I was scared stiff.

The police.

As soon as I'd hear a siren, no matter how far away it was, my stomach twisted into knots and I started shaking with fear. Usually I'd hide and peek out of my hiding place to see what it was. If it was an ambulance or a fire engine, I'd relax.

That proved that it wasn't the siren that scared me but the police.

If I was walking down the street and saw a patrol car, I'd freeze in my tracks, terrified. When that happened, I was a million times more scared than when I'd just hear a siren. I'd stand there without moving until the patrol car drove past me and disappeared from sight. Only then did my breathing slowly return to normal and I could continue on my way.

If a patrol car stopped near me, I was terrified that something bad would happen. And if I actually saw a policeman…

Don't even ask.

Everyone knew about this fear of mine. My parents tried hard to help me get over it. They also knew exactly how it started.

*   *   *

It all started when I was five.

Our whole family had gone on a trip, and we had hired the driver of a van to drive us there and back. On the way home, late at night, the driver suddenly cried out, "Oh no!"

We were all startled.

"I see a patrol car following us," he said. "I think they're signaling us to stop."

I was just a little kid and didn't really know what

a patrol car was, but I was big enough to connect my terrible fear of the police with what happened that night.

The driver stopped on the side of the road. Into the van climbed a tough-looking policeman with an evil gleam in his eyes. "Do you know why I stopped you?" he asked.

"No," said the driver.

"Are you sure you don't know?"

"Of course I'm sure," the driver answered.

"How many seats are in your vehicle?"

"Fifteen."

"And how many passengers do you have?"

"Fourteen."

"Are you sure?"

"One hundred percent," the driver said.

"Do you mind if we have a look?"

"No problem."

"Everyone out," the policeman ordered.

"Excuse me, Officer," my father said, "but do we have to get out? It will be cold outside for the little ones. Can't you count us here to see how many passengers are in the van?"

"Who said that?" the policeman asked in a voice that boded no good.

"I did," my father answered.

"Show me your ID. Now." The policeman's face twisted into a scowl when he said this.

"Certainly," my father said, reaching into his pocket.

He couldn't find his ID.

"I think I must have left it at home," I heard my father say.

"So you left it home, did you?" the policeman said in a blood-chilling tone of voice. "Okay, mister. You're under arrest."

"What?" my father cried.

"Just what you heard. Please leave the vehicle."

"But, Officer…"

The mean cop ignored my father. He just spoke into his walkie-talkie. "I have here someone resisting arrest."

Another policeman climbed into the van, and the two of them dragged my father off forcibly, even though my father said to them, "I'm willing to get off. Leave me alone."

They pulled my father off the van as I, a boy of only five, watched. I saw with my own two eyes how they handcuffed him and led him to the patrol car in disgrace.

After that, the policeman said to all of us still in the

van, "Is there anyone else here who doesn't want to get off the van?"

We all scurried off like scared rabbits. My sister and I were crying and screaming, and the policeman said to my mother, "Shut them up." But that wasn't all. He went into the van to see if any passengers were hiding inside.

When he climbed down, the driver asked him, "*Nu,* did you find any stowaways?"

"Are you mocking an officer of the law?" the policeman said gruffly.

"I'm just asking," the driver said.

The policeman started dragging the driver away, too.

"You're not going to leave them there alone on the highway, are you?" my father called out in shock.

"Ask yourself how they came to be in this situation," the policeman said.

My mother ran over and began pleading with him. "Let them go. Don't leave us here. We have small children and a baby who will freeze in this cold. Please release them. They didn't do anything wrong."

The policeman ignored her. He handcuffed the driver and pulled him over to the patrol car, then pushed him inside next to my father, and closed the door. Two other policemen got inside, and the patrol car drove away, its tires screeching.

We were left at the side of the road in the freezing cold, crying and shivering.

I looked at my mother. She didn't know what to do. I think that was the worst part for me.

After a while, my mother said, "Let's at least get back into the van so we won't be so cold."

We climbed back into the van. It was cold even inside the van, but not as cold as it was outside.

It's hard for me to describe what I felt at that moment as a child of five. What's certain is that I never forgot the scene of all of us huddling, afraid and cold, in the van, and I never, ever will.

\* \* \*

We'd been sitting there like that for an hour when I saw a patrol car approaching. We all panicked. A man got out, and it was the driver of the van. He told my mother that my father was being held at the police station. The driver said the policemen had released him only because he had warned them that if anything happened to us, the whole country would know about it — maybe even the whole world. That made them think twice about what they'd done, so they let him go.

The driver started the van and drove us all straight to the police station. My mother got out to try to convince the policemen to release my father as well.

In the end, that's what happened. Within half an hour we saw them both leaving the police station. We ran to Abba and hugged him tight. He looked very upset and angry. "I'm not going to let this go by," he said.

I was happy to see that Abba was not afraid, because it had been so hard for me to see them dragging him away and putting handcuffs on him. Believe me, no one wants to see his father like that.

On the way home, Abba said that the policemen realized they'd made a mistake, but they were too proud to get down off their "high horse." I don't remember anything else he said. I was so tired, I just fell asleep.

Now you know how I became so afraid of policemen.

*   *   *

My fear got worse as time went by. I had nightmares about policemen, and lots of times I woke up in a cold sweat. Sometimes I daydreamed about them. And whenever I heard a siren—or, worse, whenever I saw a patrol car or a policeman—my panic level shot way up.

I suffered through four and a half years of this fear. Then I turned ten.

Last summer, we went on a family vacation. My father rented a big van, but this time without a driver. My married brothers didn't go with us. It was just us children who were still at home and my mother, so my father drove.

We had a lot of fun, and on the way back, as always after a big trip, I fell asleep.

I woke up to the sound of terrible thumping. The van was rocking from side to side, and my father was struggling to control it. It was a scary feeling because we were thrown from side to side in the van when my father stepped on the brakes. Finally, he was able to stop the car.

We all breathed a sigh of relief.

My father got out of the car and walked around it. Then he came back and said to us through the open window, "We have a flat tire. It's a miracle nothing happened to us. We'll have to *bentch gomel* when we get home."

"What will we do now?" my mother asked.

"I'll have to change the flat," my father said. "Every rental car is supposed to carry a spare. But you'll all have to get out, because I'll need to lift the car with a jack."

We got out of the car. We were on a major highway, so squeezed as much as possible onto the shoulder. My mother was very worried, because the flat tire was on the left-hand side of the car, which meant that my father would have to stand on the highway side to change it.

My father took out the spare and then went to take out the jack.

I was the first one to see what was coming our way.

"Mommy!" I cried. "A patrol car is pulling up!"

*     *     *

I squeezed my eyes shut, hoping the patrol car would drive right by us. But when I opened my eyes, I discovered that my worst nightmare was heading our way. The car slowed down and stopped, and a policeman got out and walked toward my father.

I don't know what happened to me. I started to scream and go crazy. Later they told me I became hysterical, that it was a panic attack, and that I wasn't in control of what I was doing.

My screams reached the ears of the policeman, and he came over to see what was happening.

That was just what I needed.

The policeman walked toward our group, which

was standing as far back from the road as possible. My father was walking with him.

The policeman made a beeline for—guess who?

That's right. Me.

He put a hand on my shoulder and asked, "Is everything okay?"

"Aaaaargh!" I screamed like a madman. "Mommeeeee!"

The policeman looked surprised. "What happened, son? Relax. Everything's okay."

My parents explained to him that I was deathly afraid of policemen, and that for years I'd become hysterical whenever I heard a siren or saw a patrol car or a police officer.

"He never even considered the idea of a policeman coming right over to him," they told him.

The policeman was curious as to how I'd developed this fear. My father and mother looked at each other and then proceeded to tell him.

The policeman listened closely as they told him about that family trip. When they got to the part where my father was forcibly removed from the van, his expression turned serious. When they told him about the driver's arrest, he looked like he found it hard to believe. And when they told him that the policemen had left us stranded on the side of the road shivering from cold and terror, he became really angry.

"Tell me something," he said. "Did you ever submit a formal complaint?"

"No," my father said.

"Why not?"

"At the time, I wanted to. But then I thought that if the police are able to mistreat innocent people who didn't do a thing, imagine what they would do to people who filed a complaint against them."

The patrolman laughed, and then turned serious again. "Excuse the laughter," he said, "but I think you're wrong. You had a problem. You ran into a bad policeman who misused his position to harm innocent citizens. Not all policemen are like that.

"I want to find out who that policeman was, because he has no business being a member of the police force. In the meantime, I'll try to repair some of the damage he's done to our image."

\*   \*   \*

The policeman went back to the highway with my father and angled his patrol car in a way that would protect them from oncoming traffic while they changed the tire. I watched how he helped my father take off the flat, put on the spare, and store the flat tire in the trunk.

They were done in ten minutes. By then, I had calmed down. But actually I was…a little confused. On the one hand, he was a policeman. On the other hand, he seemed okay.

When they finished, the policeman came over to us again. He took off his jacket and put it on me. "Here, you can be a policeman for a few minutes," he said. He took off his hat and placed it on my head. Then he looped a chain with a police whistle on it over my neck and said to me, "Okay, Mr. Policeman, let's go. I'll show you that a patrol car isn't scary at all."

I hesitated. My father said, "I'll go with you."

With my father saying he'd come along, I agreed.

We walked over to the patrol car. The policeman sat me in the passenger seat and showed me the big computer screen where he could call up information about a driver by typing in the license plate number. He used his walkie-talkie to give all kinds of instructions to other policemen, and then he told me to push a button. I heard a siren blast. For some strange reason, the sound didn't frighten me, despite my fear of sirens.

Then he told me to push a different button, and

from the speaker came the sound of a different siren, just like the ones I was always so afraid of. But still I wasn't afraid.

I played around for another minute or two as my father and the policeman exchanged glances. After that, my mother took a picture of me wearing the policeman's uniform. When I got out of the patrol car, I discovered that it didn't scare me anymore.

The policeman shook my hand warmly. I took off the jacket and hat and gave them back to him. He got into the patrol car, and then I remembered that he'd forgotten something.

"You forgot the whistle," I said.

He smiled. "No big deal. It will be my gift to you. Whenever you're afraid of policemen, blow the whistle and remember that most policemen are good people who love children and want to help them."

* * *

That's the end of the story. And that was also the end of my fear of policemen, sirens, and patrol cars.

When I think about it, it reminds me of kids who are afraid of having iodine put on a cut. The way to help them get over the fear is to let them put on the iodine themselves. (Try it and see.)

My fear was of policemen, but as soon as I got to be a policeman myself, with a jacket, hat, and whistle, and even to turn on the siren while sitting in the patrol car, my fears disappeared as if they had never existed.

# Sudden Stop

**My name is Yoel.**

I'm twelve and a half, and I live in Jerusalem.

I'm a serious student and very popular. Actually, until recently some of the boys in my class considered me the leader. Some of them were happy about it, and others not so.

I didn't understand why some of the boys in my class didn't like me. Not that they said it to my face. They talked behind my back, but what they said made its way to my ears. I didn't react, because I wanted them to think I didn't care, but it bothered me a lot.

Don't think I was an "evil dictator" type of leader like they describe in a lot of stories. Not at all. My friends would be the first to say that I never insulted other boys or hurt their feelings, and I tried to include every single boy in our games. Still, I noticed that not everyone really liked me, and I had no idea why.

Recently something happened that made me realize something about myself, something that was the
reason some kids didn't like me.

\*   \*   \*

Every year our school holds a Gemara contest.

If you're like most kids, you get nervous before a
test. Well, a contest is a hundred times more nerve-
racking. Being quizzed in public not only tests your
memory; it also tests your ability to stay calm under
pressure. After all, you're not just in a classroom with
other kids but facing an audience of parents as well.

Every year there's a lot of excitement in our school
during the time leading up to the contest. Even the
smartest kids in class feel the tension in the air and
start to learn harder. The average learners get really
nervous and worried, while the kids who never pay
too much attention to their studies start listening better
and participating eagerly in class discussions.

That's probably the whole point of the contest. If
you want to grab the attention of those who need to
have their attention grabbed, this really does it.

The contest isn't as hard as it looks, because the
testers aren't looking to trip up kids. All the boys in
class can see exactly which questions they ask which

kids. The stronger boys get asked questions on *Rashi, Tosafos,* and even some of the other commentators. The average boys get asked questions on the Gemara alone, while the weakest boys are asked simple questions like, "One who steals from a thief is exempt from _____?" The boy needs to answer, "Paying double." Simple questions like that.

Despite this, every single boy was nervous about this contest—including me.

The day of the contest arrived. Wearing Shabbos clothes, I arrived with my parents. The school auditorium was lit up and decorated. On the stage were tables arranged in two rows one behind the other so that the audience could see all the boys. To the side was a table with places for our teacher, the principal, and the testers.

The quiz began. Tensions rose to a peak.

During the first round, the testers asked fairly easy questions. Most of the boys answered in a whisper. The testers asked them to pull the microphone close to their mouth so everyone could hear. Some kids looked like they were about to faint. Others could hardly get the words out.

Then they asked Nehorai (not his real name), the weakest student in our class, a very simple question.

The answer he gave was totally wrong. The testers tried to help him, but what he said next wasn't even related to the discussion. Kids poked each other with their elbows and laughed.

To move past the awkward moment, the teacher stated the right answer and then asked Nehorai, "Correct?"

Nehorai nodded, embarrassed.

*   *   *

I was the last one to be tested. I was coiled as tightly as a spring, waiting tensely for the question. No sooner did the question begin, though, even before the tester finished asking it, I knew that I knew the answer.

I stated the answer confidently, adding the *Rashi* and *Tosafos* for good measure. Everyone saw how the testers whispered among themselves and even smiled with pleasure. At a certain point, one of the testers stopped me. "That's enough. You've answered more than enough."

Resounding applause filled the room.

Something told me that it was no coincidence that the teacher had put me last on the list of those being tested. He knew that I knew the material very well and that I had a lot of self-confidence, and he wanted to end the first round with a good show for the parents.

I glanced at my father sitting in the audience. He gave me a serious look in return and didn't clap or give any sign of encouragement. I told myself that he was probably reacting that way because of the tense atmosphere.

The questions posed in the second round were harder. More boys stumbled over their answers or gave the wrong answer entirely. The testers usually managed to guide them to the right answer so that they wouldn't be embarrassed, but the audience could easily see who knew the material and who didn't.

Once again, Nehorai's turn came around. They asked him a question that you would ask even a third grader, but Nehorai couldn't answer it. The silence dragged on and grew uncomfortable. The examiners gave him a hint and eventually drew an answer out of him—but it was the wrong one. And I mean *totally* wrong. The other kids were so embarrassed they put their heads down on the tables.

Then it was my turn again. I was asked a very complex question. For a full four minutes I explored the Gemara with *Rashi* and *Tosafos,* noted the differences among the *meforshim,* and discussed the Maharsha's major question and several possible answers to it. As I went on, I forgot that I was in a contest. I was so sure of myself that the fact that over one hundred people were listening to me didn't faze me at all. Actually, I liked it. It felt good to have a crowd that size hanging on my every word. I finished my answer to thunderous applause.

But I was interested in the reaction of one person and one person only: my father. When I looked at him, I saw on his face an expression I'd never seen there before.

He looked furious. His eyes shot bolts of lightning. If he hadn't been my father, I might have thought that he really…that he really didn't like me at all.

\* \* \*

All the boys stood up and went over to the table of refreshments to enjoy cakes, cookies, and soft drinks with their fathers. I went over to my father, too, but he ignored me. When other fathers came up to him to congratulate him on my success, he nodded curtly, as if to say, "I heard already."

Eventually my father said to me, "Okay, Yoel. Let's go." He took my hand in his and gripped it uncomfortably, and we left.

We walked in silence. My heart was beating wildly. I'd never seen my father so angry. What was going on?

Hadn't I brought him a lot of *nachas*? Everyone was giving him compliments because of me. The other fathers would be thrilled to switch places with him!

We passed a park. My father sat down on a bench and told me to sit down next to him. Then he said, "Do you know why I'm angry?"

"No, Abba," I said. "I really don't."

"Try to think."

I sat there thinking. I thought about the answers I'd given, but I didn't think they were the problem. It was obvious that I had answered well. It dawned on me that my father must have some criticism of the way I kept on talking for such a long time, giving answers to questions I wasn't asked. I know my father. He can't stand that kind of thing and is disgusted by pride and arrogance.

"Maybe because I was showing off?" I offered.

He looked at me. "Yes, you were showing off, and, yes, I don't like that. But that's no reason for me to be angry. You know me. I'm not one to get angry. But this time you went too far. Do me a favor. Try to think about it some more and tell me what I'm angry about so that at least I'll know you have some sensitivity left."

I thought a little more, and even though I wasn't sure, I said, "Does it have something to do with Nehorai?"

"It certainly does."

"But Abba, I couldn't help him. If I would have answered instead of him—"

"No one expected you to help him, Yoel, but you smiled. A boy is in terrible distress and my son smiles! How in the world could something like that happen to me?" My father buried his face in his hands and cried.

I'd never seen my father cry before. I never thought such a thing could happen. And now it was happening right in front of me, with no warning.

"I saw that the boy was suffering," my father said. "I expected to see my son leaning forward tensely, looking worried, rooting for Nehorai to succeed in giving the right answer and getting himself out of the tight spot he was in. But no, my son was smiling. Sure, he tried to hide his smile from public view, but the fact that he had a smile on his face and not a look of distress, pain, and worry—that's what broke my heart."

We sat there in silence. Those were some of the most unpleasant moments of my life. I understood now what was bothering my father.

After a long silence, my father grew calm, and then he said to me, "I want to tell you a story that happened when I was a boy, about forty years ago."

\*   \*   \*

I lived on a small moshav in the south (said my father) and learned in the same class as a boy I'll call Sruli. Sruli was the son of the village's rabbi, a true tzaddik who was known far beyond the borders of our small village.

Sruli himself was a genius, and he applied himself to his learning. He was the top boy in our class by far. He would pay attention in class from beginning to end, learn for hours after school, yet he still found the time to lead our games and organize things like the Lag BaOmer bonfire and class parties.

Along with being smart, studious, and a leader, Sruli was also no small prankster. Not that there's a contradiction, but with him the contrast was striking. He got into all kinds of mischief, always pulling pranks and playing practical jokes. It was like there were two Srulis: the serious learner who concentrated in class and the prankster, the troublemaker.

The biggest prank he ever pulled was when we were twelve.

You might not know it, but back then on a moshav, fifteen-year-olds drove tractors. Not only did they have their father's permission, but they even helped with plowing the fields. It was a normal part of life and perfectly legal.

Though we were younger, only twelve years old, we all knew how to drive a tractor, and, of course, none of us would dare drive it anywhere but in the field, with our fathers supervising.

Sruli had a friend who wasn't a boy in our class or even in our school. Actually, he wasn't a boy or even a teen or young man. He was an elderly man over seventy years old, and his name was Tuvia.

Everyone called him "Tuvia the milkman," though he didn't do any milking.

Tuvia had an old truck that served as the moshav's only form of transportation. He used the truck to bring supplies, like food items for our store and chicken feed, or to move furniture. He was also the village's official driver. Say, for instance, there was a wedding. They'd ask Tuvia to drive the guests to the hall. He would push all the junk in the back to the side, pull down the benches for the guests to sit on, and that's how we'd be driven to the wedding, surrounded by the smells of the produce whose expiration date had long since passed, trying unsuccessfully to make sure our shoes didn't get dirty from the fertilizer and chicken feed.

Those were the days. Believe me, Yoel, those weddings were far more beautiful and joyous than any of the fancy weddings you see today. You'd wear your

Shabbos pants and a nice shirt, either yours or your neighbor's. Most people didn't have more than one pair of pants and one shirt for Shabbos. You'd wear your regular everyday shoes, polished to a shine, because most people didn't have Shabbos shoes then. That's how we'd travel, on that bench in the piece of junk owned and driven by Tuvia the milkman.

Sruli discovered Tuvia when he needed his help. That is, it was when Tuvia needed Sruli's help to carry something. From then on, Sruli went with him on his many local outings.

Sruli's father, who as I said was the rav of our village, allowed this, perhaps because he realized that his Sruli needed some breathing space to calm his turbulent soul. No one envied Sruli this special friendship, probably because none of the other children took any interest in Tuvia the milkman, or in anyone over the age of bar mitzvah for that matter. It made sense that it was Sruli, the smartest and friendliest boy in our class, who spent time with Tuvia. We didn't think there was any reason to be jealous of him.

It happened one rainy day. I don't know what was going through Sruli's mind, but he went over to Tuvia's truck—which was unlocked, like all the tractors on the moshav, and all the homes, for that matter—climbed up into the driver's seat, and turned the key in the ignition.

After a few false starts, the engine caught, and the truck started to move forward. It reached the moshav's center, where a date palm stood inside a large circle of grass. We were sitting there and didn't notice who was driving the truck until Sruli shouted out to us, "Want a ride? Get in!"

As you can imagine, it was strange to see Sruli driving Tuvia's truck, but since he told us to get in, we did. We didn't think about how dangerous it was.

He started to drive around the circle and did it about thirty times until our heads were spinning. Then he turned down one of the streets.

What happened on the way was that Sruli got very excited about driving and he drove wildly. He was on top of the world. When he passed someone from class or school, he stopped and called out to him to hop on, and then continued on his way. From time to time the engine sputtered to a stop, and Sruli started it again.

By the time he'd driven around the moshav for half an hour, there were twenty children on the truck. Without knowing how it happened, Sruli found himself driving on the main road that ran outside the moshav.

When he had been driving around the moshav, he'd driven slowly. Now he picked up speed.

We sat there enjoying every minute of the ride, having a great time. We had no idea it was dangerous. We sang at the top of our lungs, stood up and danced, and fell all over ourselves when Sruli came to a sudden stop or the engine died.

Looking back on it today, I consider it a miracle that nothing bad happened to us. It could have ended in tragedy. That ride was the most dangerous thing I've ever done in my life. Though Sruli was tall and could reach the pedals—I know because he bragged to us, "Hey, I can reach the pedals!"—the bottom line is that a twelve-year-old boy was driving a truck with twenty boys in the back.

A sudden rainstorm caught us by surprise. Sruli couldn't figure out how to turn on the windshield wipers, and it could very well be that there weren't any. He was now driving blind, trying to guess where the road was. The truck started weaving from side to side.

Even this didn't bother us. We still had no idea of the danger we were in.

All of a sudden, I saw a man walking along the road, holding an umbrella. Sruli said to us, "Hold on tight, because I'm going to stop for him."

"It's an adult," I told him, but Sruli remembered that Tuvia gave rides to anyone he saw on the road. He slowed down and beeped, and then stopped next to the pedestrian with the umbrella.

"Want a ride?" he shouted for the twenty-first time. "Get in!"

The man turned around and tilted back his umbrella, revealing his face.

It was none other than our principal!

If there was any danger to our lives on that wild ride it was right then. For one simple reason.

We were about to die of fright.

But Sruli was so drunk with happiness he didn't know the difference between "cursed is Haman" and "blessed is Mordechai"—Rabbi Mordechai Stein, that is, our principal. Even discovering the man's identity didn't dampen his enthusiasm. "Would the principal like a ride?" he shouted. "I'm going to the moshav. Why walk in the rain?"

If Rabbi Stein was surprised to see one of his students driving a truck, and shocked to see half his school hanging out the windows, this question threw him completely off balance. And I'm not speaking metaphorically. He rocked from side to side and fell into a puddle.

Sruli didn't miss a beat. He jumped down from the truck and extended a helping hand to the man sprawled in the mud.

It struck us right then that though Sruli hadn't lost his cool, he'd lost the truck. He'd forgotten to pull the hand brake, and the truck started to move forward, driverless.

"Jump off!" Sruli screamed. "Get out fast! It's dangerous!"

And jump we did, one after the other, landing on top of each other. Fortunately, the truck was moving on level ground, and not on an incline, so it moved very slowly. I don't want to think of what might have happened if it had gone down a hill with all of us inside.

We stood there on the side of the road looking on in disbelief as the empty truck escaped to freedom, wandering like a bird flying across the wilderness, as if knowing this was its last flight.

The truck continued to move away from us until it disappeared around the bend, and since it didn't know it was a bend, it continued straight ahead, crossed the shoulder, and drove off the road into a ravine.

The truck rolled down into the ravine and crashed with an explosive sound louder than the thunder and lightning of the storm, but not louder than our pounding hearts. We knew exactly what would have happened to us had we stayed on that truck. For the first time that day, we realized what a stupid thing Sruli—and we, his partners in crime—had done.

We stood there, twenty-one children and one principal, who was now standing up. His anger and shock gave way to worry.

"Are you absolutely certain no one remained in the truck?" he asked.

"I'm almost positive," Sruli said, knowing that for the very first time in his life he'd given the wrong answer.

*Almost?*

We all ran to the curve in the road and immediately saw the truck—or what was left of it. It had broken into thousands of big, little, and medium pieces. We clambered down the incline to look among the debris for a boy or even part of one, but fortunately we didn't find anyone, and in that strange inspection we made, we discovered that, yes, all of us were alive and well.

We started walking back to the moshav with the principal, but somehow we weren't afraid or shaking with fear. After the scary experience we'd just gone through, there was no point in being afraid of anything else.

Sruli walked in silence. He was in shock.

"Does anyone have any idea what Tuvia will do now?" the principal asked.

We weren't sure if he was worried about Tuvia or about his outstanding yet rebellious pupil Sruli, the son of the village's rav.

When we got there, we said good-bye, and the principal said to Sruli, "You realize that I'm going to tell your father, don't you?"

Sruli nodded and disappeared into his house. The rest of us also ran to our houses and disappeared inside.

I walked through the front door casually, as if nothing had happened. My parents didn't ask me where I'd been, so I didn't have to answer that question.

All that night I wondered what would happen to Sruli. I wasn't the only one. All the other kids thought about it, too.

The next day, when he walked into the classroom, we all surrounded him.

"They really gave it to you, didn't they?" I said to him, meaning that he must have gotten a good spanking. All of us knew that that was what he deserved. It's not like now. Back then, when a child did something really wrong, it was obvious he'd get punished for it.

"Nope," Sruli said, surprising us all. "I didn't get punished."

We believed him and didn't think he was hiding the truth from us. What would be the point? Getting spanked was such an accepted thing that there was no reason for him to deny it.

Sruli told us what happened, but only briefly. We had to wait several years before we found out the full story.

It turned out that Tuvia had paid his father a visit and told him what had happened to his truck and who had brought it to its early end. Sruli's father, the village rabbi, was a highly respected individual whose name is known by everyone, even today. He sat with Tuvia and they discussed compensation.

Tuvia argued that according to the halachah, the rabbi wasn't obligated to pay for his son's damages. The rabbi told him that as long as he was still rabbi, he'd be the one to decide whether or not to pay. They agreed that Tuvia would find out the price of a new truck, as would the rabbi, to prevent Tuvia from quoting a lower price to his own detriment.

That's how the conversation went, more or less, between those two wonderful people.

When they finished talking, Tuvia went into Sruli's

room and looked at him long and hard. "What you did wasn't like you at all," he said. "It's more like something a juvenile delinquent would do. You have hurt and disappointed both me and your father. You need to get back on track."

Sruli started to cry.

After he'd cried for about an hour, his father called him into his room. Sruli knew he was in for a good spanking, and he was scared stiff.

"You stole a vehicle that wasn't yours from a person who trusted you," his father said to him. "Do you realize how seriously wrong that was?"

Sruli nodded.

"What you did is terrible. I'm very angry with you. That's not the way a *frum*, well-brought-up Jewish boy acts. Do you promise me that such a thing will not happen again?"

Sruli cried and promised that something like that would *never* happen again.

Then his father said, "You drove without permission and without a license, putting yourself in danger. You violated the Torah directive to guard your life. In addition, you broke the law. If a policeman had stopped you, you would have been charged. Do you realize that?"

Again Sruli nodded.

"I want you to promise me that you will never do something like that again."

Sruli promised.

"You endangered not only the lives of the twenty children who rode with you in the truck, but you also endangered the many other children and adults who could have been run over. That's a criminal offense and so irresponsible as to be almost unforgivable. You almost brought a disaster on the whole village. If anything had happened, do you know what the halachah is for someone who kills accidently? True, in our times there are no cities of refuge, but I'm telling you that if such a thing had happened, I would have taken the whole family and left the moshav to exile myself to a place where no one knew me. Do you understand what that would have meant?"

Sruli burst into tears at hearing his father's rebuke.

"Do you promise me that you will never involve others in doing something wrong or put them in danger?"

Sruli promised.

"Now go to sleep," his father said.

Sruli was astonished. What was going on? Why hadn't his father spanked him?

That was what was really bothering him. He assumed that a few *potches* were a suitable punishment for the seriously bad thing he had done.

His father's words settled deeply in his mind and heart. He went to bed, did a lot of thinking, and came to the conclusion that his real punishment was that his father had withheld his hand.

\* \* \*

A week later, Tuvia drove up in a new truck that was a big improvement over the first one. He looked pretty pleased, and everyone realized that he had, after all, gained from the whole episode. Sruli's father, the village rabbi, had compensated him so well that he'd been able to buy himself a truck that was much bigger and better than the battered old piece of junk he'd once had.

In time, people forgot about the incident.

A year and a half went by.

During that year and a half, we grew up. Some of us became bar mitzvah, and we all became mature and serious. Toward the end of eighth grade, there was a big test. It was on many pages of Gemara with *Rashi, Tosafos,* and *meforshim.*

We reviewed, learned with *chavrusas,* worked hard,

clarified, ate, slept, and dreamed Gemara. During those weeks before the test, we lived and breathed Gemara.

The day of the exam arrived.

We were to be tested by the principal, a renowned *talmid chacham*, and by Sruli's father, the rabbi of the village.

The first round began. All the boys knew the material, but one boy in particular stood head and shoulders above the others with his brilliant answers. It was Sruli, of course.

When he was asked a question, he answered by quoting the Gemara, related passages found in other *masechtos*, *Rashi*, and *Tosafos*, and then went on to discuss the *meforshim'* difficulties and their resolution of those difficulties. The principal, who seemed to have heard of Sruli, sailed with him to vistas we could only dream of— *meforshim* we hadn't been taught, differences of opinion, reasonings, and disputes we knew about only from an older brother or our father. It was a spectacular display. Every time it was Sruli's turn, we looked at him, but we also watched his father.

For some reason, his father didn't react. Not a muscle moved in his face.

*    *    *

"Sound familiar, Yoel?" my father asked me.

I nodded, and my father continued with the story.

\*   \*   \*

We couldn't figure out why the rabbi didn't seem happy with his outstanding son who was bringing him so much *nachas*. For some reason, he looked like he was suffering.

The test ended, and we were sent home to rest after the difficult period of studying for the test.

But there was something in the air that ruined the festive atmosphere: the rabbi's ignoring his son. Everyone seemed to think it was connected with the truck incident, but most of the kids said that the rabbi wouldn't hold a grudge against his own son for behavior that was in the past and forgotten.

\*   \*   \*

A week later, I found out what had happened.

The night after the test, the rav again called his son into his study and said to him, "Did you look at me during the test?"

"Yes," Sruli answered.

"What did you see?"

"You looked angry."

"Do you have any idea why?" the rav asked his son.

"Absolutely none," Sruli answered. "I knew everything! I quoted word for word, I—"

"I'm not deaf." His father cut him off sharply in a way so unlike him that Sruli was startled. "I heard and I saw and I listened, and I could have had a lot of *nachas*. But I didn't. Instead I had a lot of pain and anguish. Do you have any idea why?"

Sruli had no idea why.

The rav gave a deep, heartbreaking sigh and then said, "The Creator of the world blessed me with a son of great ability. But I wonder if He needed to make him so talented."

Sruli looked at him, puzzled. He didn't understand why his father was complaining about Hashem blessing him with ability.

"You have no idea what I'm talking about, do you?" his father asked him.

"No, Abba. I don't understand. I really don't understand what's upsetting you."

"I'll tell you. During the rounds of questioning, there was one boy who had a hard time answering. Do you know who I'm talking about?"

"Yes," Sruli said. "You must mean Yossi."

"Yes. Yossi stumbled over his answers, and I tried not to look at him. I was hoping he'd remember something, or at least that the examiner would help him. For a split second, I happened to glance your way. Do you know what I saw?"

Sruli didn't answer.

"I saw a smile on your face. Not a big one, or even a little one. It was more the flicker of a smile that showed a certain satisfaction with your friend's downfall. That is what caused me such anguish.

"During the next round, when Yossi was asked a question, he got nervous. He tried to answer, but he stuttered and stammered and got stuck. It was obvious that he had no familiarity with the subject.

"I looked at you again. I saw the glimmer of a smile, and my heart broke completely. Hashem gave me a son blessed with talents and abilities, but if he doesn't have a heart or soul, I don't want his talents and abilities."

And then the rabbi reached out and slapped Sruli across the cheek. Sruli burst out crying and ran to his room.

For the next two days, he walked around totally broken. Not because of the slap, but because of a nagging question.

Two days later, his father walked into his room, sat

down on the bed, and said to him, "You haven't had a minute's peace since our last conversation, have you?"

Sruli nodded.

"You're wondering why I slapped you now and not after the terrible thing you did with the truck, aren't you?"

Sruli nodded again.

"I'll tell you," the rabbi said. "A boy can be as mischievous as anything, but he'll outgrow it and become more serious and settled. I knew that no matter how seriously wrong your actions were with the truck, they didn't stem from badness but from impulsivity. So, even though I was obligated to reprimand you for it, I didn't think it right to give you a spanking, because I knew that it was only a matter of time until you'd mature and realize yourself that what you'd done was very wrong.

"But it's different when it comes to *middos*. They tend to grow stronger with time, not disappear. When I see my son smiling at another person's downfall, I can't let it pass without comment. That's why I *potched* you for the first time in your life, so that you'd realize that something terrible had happened.

"I'm a little ashamed to say it," his father continued, "but I'm almost happy that the truck crashed and cost me so much money, because now you have the chance to compare that incident with how I view your behavior toward a weaker boy. Compare my reaction then with my strong reaction now. I expect you to find a way to right this wrong."

\* \* \*

And fix it he did. Sruli asked Yossi to forgive him and arranged to learn with him. They continued learning together for many years. They learned together in yeshivah and kept it up until Yossi got married and moved to a different city.

The learning partnership between Sruli and Yossi gave a lot to Yossi. He developed into an unbelievably strong learner and went from being less than average to outstanding. He went on to become a real *ben Torah* whose *hasmadah* and desire to grow in learning carried him far beyond his natural abilities.

Interestingly, his natural abilities seemed to increase as time went on and he began using more of his potential. Yossi's children were all excellent students who suffered none of his learning difficulties. Actually, they were outstanding and gave him a lot of *nachas*.

Two people benefited from the study partnership: Yossi gained in scholarship, and Sruli, in good *middos*.

My father finished his story, and I sat there

spellbound. It was really an amazing story. I'd never heard anything like it.

I got the point. I knew the message my father wanted me to take out of that story. He was comparing me with Sruli, the brilliant boy who was stupid when it came to his friend's distress. I saw clearly that my father had treated me just like the rabbi of the moshav, Sruli's father, except for…the slap. Our parents don't hit us.

We sat there in silence. All of sudden, a big question about the story popped into my mind.

"Abba," I asked, "how do you know so many details about Sruli's conversations with his father? About the truck and the way he acted during the test? Did he tell everyone?"

"No," my father said, "he didn't tell everyone. He told only Yossi. When he came to apologize to Yossi and suggested that they learn together, he told him the whole story. That's what made Yossi believe him when he said he was sorry and made him willing to forgive him and even become his best friend."

"Does that mean…?" I looked at my father in disbelief.

"My name is Yosef Chaim, isn't it? I'm Yossi, the boy who lacked talent, who stumbled over his answers during the test. Sruli's story is my story, too. If not for Sruli's father, the rabbi of the village, where would I be today?

"Now, do you have any ideas about what you plan to do with this story?"

"Yes, Abba," I said. "I have an idea. I'm going to do just what Sruli did. Plus something else."

My father raised his eyebrows.

"I'm going to tell this story to kids everywhere so that they'll know how important it is to see the other person and not to ignore his pain and for sure not to smile at his failure."

That's it, kids. Here's the story. Do with it as you see fit.

# The Memory Card

**My name is Baruch.**

I'm eleven, and I live in Beit Shemesh.

I'm a fairly good student, friendly, full of life and action. Most of all, I love going on trips.

I get it from my father. He takes us on trips all the time to places all over Israel. We pack up food, water, hats, and hiking gear and go hiking down streams and dry riverbeds called wadis. My father makes sure the whole family is careful to follow all the safety rules.

There's something else I really like, and I have to tell you about it right now or I won't be able to start the story.

I like to take pictures.

I've had a camera since I was seven (upgraded to the latest model every couple of years). At any opportunity, I take pictures of anything that moves or even things that don't.

You understand without my telling you that on trips the camera doesn't leave my hand. I take hundreds of pictures on each trip. Once, my sister joked that she pities me because I see the whole trip through the camera lens while the rest of the family sees it in real life.

I thought about what she said. There was a lot of truth to it, but it didn't change how I felt or what I wanted to do. I came up with a good answer to give her, too.

"You see the trip just once, but I see it again and again and again."

Actually, that's not one hundred percent true. Yes, I like to take pictures, and I like to look at them later, too, but…well, I don't always get around to it. I'm sure that's not news to you.

We all like to take tons of pictures, but they stay stored on the memory card and we hardly ever develop them.

My father said that when he was growing up cameras used film. Every roll of film had twenty-four or thirty-six pictures, and the most you'd use on a trip was one roll.

"Right after the trip, we'd give in the roll of film to be developed," he told me. "We'd have to wait a few days to see them, not a few minutes, but you can still see those pictures in my old albums."

"I don't get it," I said. "How did you choose what to take a picture of? I can take twenty shots of the same thing. I can take five hundred pictures on one trip and still feel like I missed something."

My father answered that that was the difference between now and then. Then, everyone had less, but everyone was satisfied and didn't feel that they were missing anything. Today, children have everything they want, but everyone feels that he's losing out on something.

That's really true, especially when you think that no matter how many pictures I take, it's hard for me to enjoy them because most of them are never printed and never will be.

Now for the story.

\*    \*    \*

It happened on a trip to Mount Hermon last winter.

We heard that the snow was several feet deep on the Hermon, so there was no question but that we'd make the trip. Where we live, in Beit Shemesh, it rarely snows, and if it does, only a couple of inches fall.

We left early in the morning in our minivan. We

knew it would be a long trip, but it felt even longer than we'd thought. Even when it seemed that we were getting close, we still had to keep driving, because it took us a full hour to get from the bottom of the Hermon to the top.

I took pictures the whole time, from the first turn up the mountain to the snowy peaks stretched out before us. I shot picture after picture nonstop.

Finally, we got out of the car and we built a huge snowman. I probably took around a hundred pictures, from every possible angle, just of that.

I checked the camera. There were five hundred and sixty-seven pictures in it. I'd never gotten to a number as big as that.

We headed back to the car that afternoon, tired but happy.

My little brother, who's a year younger than I am, asked to see the pictures. I told him to wait until we got home and I could back them up. Then he could look at them as much as he wanted.

But he pestered me until I gave in. I handed him the camera with a warning to just flip through the pictures without pushing any buttons that might erase them.

My brother started flipping through the pictures. When we reached the car, he sat next to me, and I saw that he was playing around with the camera, but I didn't have the energy to pay too much attention to what he was doing. I was really tired, and my eyes sort of closed on their own. Soon I was fast asleep.

*   *   *

I woke up an hour later to the sounds of a discussion going on in the car.

"Give it to me. I know how it works," one of my brothers said.

"No, give it to Rivky. She knows how to use it."

The more I woke up, the more it dawned on me that they were talking about my camera.

"Is everything okay?" I asked.

"Not exactly," my older brother said. "The pictures are gone."

"What?"

I grabbed the camera and turned it on. I knew better than any of them how to use it, so it didn't take me long to discover that someone—and it wasn't hard to guess who—must have pushed one button too many: the Delete button.

I quickly opened the camera to take out the memory card, thinking that maybe there would be some way to restore the missing pictures.

The memory card slot was empty.

"Where's the memory card?" I asked.

"I don't know. I opened the camera back in the parking lot, when we ate, because I wanted to see the pictures from the beginning. I saw the memory card, and suddenly it disappeared on me."

I'd never felt as angry as I did at that moment.

Everyone looked at me. To avoid my anger, my younger brother moved to the back seat, switching places with my sister. It didn't help. I said a few choice words that I'd rather not repeat here, because I'm too ashamed. They were mean words that kids sometimes say when they're very, very angry.

Everyone shouted at me, "How can you say such a thing?"

Okay, so I didn't really mean that I would _____ him, but I wanted to hit him hard to show how angry I was. So even though we were driving, I tried to climb into the back seat to pummel my brother. My sister Rivky held me back so I couldn't reach him. Everyone knew that if I made it into the back seat, he'd be in big trouble.

Rivky said to my father, "Abba, can you please stop the car? I want to talk to Baruch alone for a minute."

My father pulled over to the shoulder, where it was

safe to stop. I didn't want to get out of the car, but my father and my older brother dragged me out.

"Get out this minute," said my brother. "You'll think about what to do about him later."

I stood there next to the car, fuming, and Rivky said, "Let's go for a little walk."

\* \* \*

Let me tell you a little bit about my sister Rivky. She's like a mother to us. She takes care of us, cooks, does laundry, cleans the house, and helps us with homework. My mother works hard at an outside job, and Rivky is her biggest helper. My sister has good *middos*, too. She's a real *tzaddeikes* and very special, and everyone likes and admires her.

There's another thing that's important to know about Rivky. She's twenty-seven and still not married. Don't ask me why. My father says that she's so special that we just didn't find the right boy for her.

We all respect Rivky, and that's the reason I agreed to talk to her. Not for a minute did I think she'd calm me down, but I said to myself, *At the very least she deserves my respect.*

"I once read that if a person controls his anger," Rivky told me, "he can, at that very minute, ask for something big and Hashem will answer him favorably. I know that you're very angry. And your anger is justified. You took a lot of pictures and kindly let him look at them by himself. You also warned him to be careful. But he ignored your warning, and now you've lost all the pictures that were so important to you. You can be as angry with him as you want, and even feel like hitting him, but that won't bring back your pictures.

"On the other hand, you now have an opportunity: to rein in your anger and ask Hashem for something you really, really want. I'm certain you'll gain much more from that."

I was about to say something back when suddenly I had a brainstorm. "No problem," I said. "I'm going to ask Hashem for something, and I hope He will take into consideration that I'm giving up my anger and will give me what I ask for."

"Okay," Rivky said. "Go ahead and ask. You probably don't want me to hear."

"No, I *do* want you to hear. But only you." And then I said, "I ask Hashem to please take into consideration that I am overcoming my anger and to please bring my dear sister Rivky bas Chava a *zivug hagun* within a month. Signed, Baruch."

Rivky burst out laughing. I guess she thought my

saying "signed" was funny. Then she said, "You're so cute. You wasted this moment on me?"

"If I'd have asked for something else, that would have been a waste," I told her. "Right now, the most important thing in the world to me and to all of us is that you find a good *shidduch*."

Rivky hugged me. "I really appreciate that, Baruch. You warmed my heart. Let's go back and keep this to ourselves, okay?"

"Of course," I said, petrified at the thought of anyone finding out.

We went back. I clamped my lips shut as I slid into my seat. No one could understand what had come over me.

My father asked, "Is everything okay?"

I nodded and even managed to squeeze out a small smile so that everyone would know I wasn't mad anymore.

"Rivky, how did you do it?" someone asked, to which Rivky replied, "It wasn't me. It was his decision."

As we drove, I talked to my younger brother, who was sitting scrunched up in fear. "Relax," I said to him. "Everything's okay."

My brother was surprised, and from that moment on, the ice was broken. Double meaning, because we were far enough away from the Hermon to take off our gloves and jackets.

* * *

We arrived home, and I started to count the days until my sister found a *shidduch*.

A week passed, then two, but nothing.

One day we got a phone call. The caller was a *bachur* whose parents davened in our shul.

"Hello," he said. "Did you perhaps lose a memory card at the Hermon?"

"Yes, we did," my mother said. "Did you find it?"

"No," he said, "but I happened to be visiting an American friend, Eliezer, who learns in a yeshivah here, and he told me he found a memory card with a lot of pictures. He showed the pictures to every Israeli he met, hoping that someone would recognize the people in them. When he showed them to me, I recognized your family right away."

"Wonderful!" my mother said. "Do you have the memory card?"

"No," he said, "Eliezer still has it. But I have his phone number, and you can arrange to meet with him. Maybe you'll be going to Yerushalayim or he'll be in Beit Shemesh."

When my mother told me the good news, I was happy but also a little disappointed. After the "deal" I'd made with Hashem, I'd have preferred to get what I asked for instead of getting back the memory card.

But I didn't tell that to anyone.

My mother called the *bachur* and found out that he had no plans to be in Beit Shemesh. It was decided that my father and I would travel the next day to his yeshivah to get the card.

\*　　\*　　\*

The next afternoon, we arrived at the yeshivah. It was a yeshivah for American *bachurim* who come to learn in Eretz Yisrael for several years.

We went into the yeshivah and found Eliezer. He was nice, and his Hebrew was really good. He told us that he'd been on the Hermon with a few friends and that he'd found the memory card in the parking lot. My father asked him how his Hebrew came to be so fluent, and he said that he'd been learning in Jerusalem for several years and was used to speaking Hebrew.

Eliezer gave me the memory card. I thanked him and gave him a *sefer* that my father had edited. My father talked with him a little bit more, and then we said good-bye.

My father didn't say much on the drive home. I could see he was thinking about something.

When we got home, my father, my mother, and my sister Rivky had a discussion.

Several weeks passed. One evening, my sister called the house to say it was final. She was engaged.

As you can guess, no one was happier than I, except maybe Rivky and her *chasan*, Eliezer.

The *l'chaim* took place exactly two months after my decision to control my anger. Several weeks later, we celebrated their *vort*.

Our family had gotten a very big present: a happy bride and a groom who was a *ben Torah* from an excellent family.

*   *   *

Several days after the engagement, I talked with Rivky. She thanked me again and said that she felt it was all thanks to me. It was easy to see that the lost memory card was what had led to finding her *bashert* from across the ocean, where they wouldn't have even thought of looking.

I told Rivky that I wasn't totally okay with the deal I'd made. I gave up the memory card so that she would get engaged, but in the end, the memory card was returned to me and she also got engaged, so I felt like I was still in debt.

Rivky laughed. "What a great kid you are," she said. Then she became serious and said, "No, Baruch. You didn't make a deal about the memory card. Losing a memory card is too small a price to pay. You made a deal about your anger, which was much harder for you to give up than the memory card. Don't you agree?"

I thought about what she said and nodded.

"Do you know how much people are willing to lose because of anger and jealousy and other bad *middos*? There are people who know that if they apologize they stand to benefit, but they still don't do it. There are people who know that if they drop their anger toward a certain person, that person will be good to them in return—yet still they prefer to stay angry. Anger is a very bad *middah* that mainly destroys the person who is angry. Even so, people hang on to their bad *middos* and refuse to give them up.

"But you, Baruch, you let go of your anger at its peak, when it was burning hot inside you. When you did that, you came through on your part of the deal, and now you got paid back with interest.

"Now the whole family owes you one for controlling

your anger. I think that in the future you'll decide on your own to let go and not hurt others back when they hurt you. You'll see that Hashem will reward you again and again in all sorts of ways."

*   *   *

What my amazing sister Rivky said I want to tell kids everywhere. We all have situations in life when we feel like hitting or hurting or insulting back. It turns out that we gain a lot more by conquering those impulses than by giving in to them.

Eliezer came to our house the Shabbos after the engagement. He gave each one of us kids a present, but he saved the best and most expensive for last, to give to me.

"I know it's not nice to play favorites," Eliezer said, "but I talked it over with your brothers and sisters, and they all agreed that you deserve this present, not only because you controlled yourself when it mattered, but because you have a share in our *shidduch*. Though someone else got the *shadchan gelt*, everyone who helps make a *shidduch*, even in part, deserves something, so please accept this gift."

I opened the package with trembling hands. Inside the box sat an expensive camera from the States, better than any I'd ever had, the kind I'd never even dreamed of owning.

"There's something else."

Eliezer opened a small box and took out a 32GB memory card. On it was pasted a sticker with one word written on it: "Remember."

I knew exactly what they wanted me to remember. Not the memory card, but a memory much more meaningful.

# Afikoman Mystery

**My name is Binyamin.**

I'm twelve, and I live in Bnei Brak.

I'm a kid who's interested in everything, especially solving mysteries—and that's what my story is about.

My story is connected with Pesach, too. Or, to be more exact, with the *afikoman*, as I'm sure you've guessed.

Every year, I'm the one who finds the *afikoman*. Don't ask me how. I have my methods. From the minute we get to *Yachatz*, when my father and Reb Henich, our elderly neighbor who is a regular guest in our home, take out the matzah, I keep my eyes glued on both of them. I watch their every move and spot all their attempts to distract us. Their tricks might work for the other kids, but not me. Usually, I succeed in discovering the hiding place.

With my father, it's not that hard. I guess, like most

fathers, he doesn't really care if the *afikoman* is found. Actually, he *wants* it to be found, and the sooner the better, so that the children will return to the Seder table and not keep running around looking for it. That's probably why my father makes every "mistake" that possibly could be made by someone who wants to hide something. Usually, it doesn't take long for us to find his hiding place. Short of declaring loudly that the *afikoman* is "on top of the refrigerator behind the matzah," my father does just about everything to make sure we'll find it.

With Reb Henich, it's a different story.

Reb Henich guards the *afikoman* as if it were the gold in Fort Knox. From the minute the Seder begins, I see signs that our neighbor is worried about where he'll hide it this time. When we get to *Yachatz*, I start worrying about his health. He gets very nervous, as if our finding the *afikoman* would be a personal failure on his part. He takes it really seriously, deliberately misleading us, and in the end he hides it in a place where it's impossible, and I mean really impossible, to find.

For anyone but me, of course.

Honestly, there were years when even I didn't find it. We reached *Tzafun*, and Reb Henich went dramatically to the hiding place, which he managed to keep secret even as he retrieved the *afikoman*. Then he would eat the *afikoman* with great satisfaction while we watched in dismay, disappointed that he didn't have to give us anything.

Once I complained about it to my father.

"Look how much pleasure he gets from it," my father said to me. "Let him enjoy the satisfaction. After all, he gives you all a nice book every holiday. What else does he have aside from these small pleasures?"

But we kids didn't see it that way. I made it my personal mission, especially in recent years, to find his hiding places. And I succeeded, year after year.

Three years ago I didn't find it, but just before *Tzafun*, Reb Henich dozed off, and I used those few seconds to slip a piece of matzah from the *afikoman* bag hidden in his *kittel*.

Well, that made our guest really mad. He said with irritation, "You didn't find the *afikoman*, you stole it."

"As long as the *afikoman* hasn't been eaten yet," I said, "it's considered that I found it."

We both started arguing if it was or wasn't considered my find. But one look from my father made it clear to me that I was getting close to chutzpah. My father and I have this look between us that lets me know that I've reached the limit. Even though I'd done it all with a smile, that look was enough for me to know that I'd taken things too far and should drop it. (I suggest you ask your parents for a "look" like that, because it's a kind of signal, like a secret code between your parents and you telling you that you need to stop doing the wrong thing you're doing.)

\*   \*   \*

The next year, Reb Henich came to our Seder armed for battle. He maintained eye contact with me right from the beginning. At a certain point, he left to take care of something. That was my signal that he was looking for a hiding place. All the other years I'd had some idea of where to look, but now he went through the whole house. He went up, down, under, and over, and at his age it wasn't easy. Finally, he returned to the Seder table, looking tired but pleased as punch.

I went to the last place he'd been, the children's room. I looked through it the way only I know how to look, but I didn't find anything.

I realized that Reb Henich had tricked me. He'd hidden the *afikoman* before he got to the children's room, and he'd only gone there to fool me. I remembered that he'd been in the laundry room. I searched it thoroughly, but I didn't find the *afikoman*. From there I worked backward, going to all the places Reb Henich had been, but I came up empty-handed.

A while later I made another search, but still came up with nothing. The *afikoman* was gone.

I was so disappointed and tired from all the searching that something happened that had never happened before. I went to my room to rest a little, and I fell asleep.

Until the morning!

When I woke up, it took me a little while to realize that it was Pesach and that the Seder was over and I hadn't been there for the end, and that, worst of all, I'd missed out on two *afikomans*!

I was so disappointed I started to cry. My mother came into the room and tried to console me.

"Abba buys you *afikoman* presents anyway," she said, "so what's all the moaning and groaning?"

I explained to her that it wasn't about the present. "The whole point is for me to find the *afikoman*," I sobbed.

"Why is it so important to you?" she asked. "You get the gift anyway."

"I don't know," I said. "Do you think they made

this a *minhag* for nothing? I'm the proof that looking for the *afikoman* really excites kids and keeps them interested."

My mother laughed. "But why did you take the *afikoman* out of Reb Henich's *kittel* last year?"

"Because he went too far in the way he hid the *afikoman*," I said, really angry now. "He has to show us some consideration."

"Let me see if I understand what you're saying," my mother said. "A minute ago you said that searching for the *afikoman* is exciting for you and that you don't want to get a present for nothing. Now you're saying that you want Reb Henich to hide it, but not make it so hard to find… Do you think you might be fooling yourself a little?"

I had all kinds of answers, none of them good ones. I tried telling my mother that games have levels, and that I wanted the level of difficulty adjusted to one that suited me.

But no sooner were the words out of my mouth than I realized how I sounded. I sounded like a bossy kid who wants to make sure everything goes his way, according to his own crazy rules. I pressed my lips shut and didn't say another word.

My mother looked at me and obviously guessed

what I was thinking. All she said was, "Got it?"

I sure did. But I can't say it made me happy.

*   *   *

All this happened two years ago. Now I'm coming to the Pesach of last year.

If anything, I was looking forward to finding the *afikoman* more than ever, but with one major difference. I made up my mind that this time I wouldn't get upset about anything but would just try very hard to find Reb Henich's *afikoman*. Without any discounts or levels of difficulty.

*Kadesh* arrived, then *Urchatz*, *Karpas*, and *Yachatz*. Reb Henich broke his middle matzah in two and hid the piece for the *afikoman* in a satin bag designed especially for that.

Then he did exactly what he'd done the previous year. He went through the whole house and returned five minutes later looking pleased with himself.

I started my expedition, and let me tell you, there wasn't an inch of the house that escaped my search.

After three rounds of searching, I went back to the children's room, where there's a small space between the top of the closet and the ceiling. I'd never thought of that spot as a possibility before, because how could

the elderly Reb Henich get to it? But then I noticed the ladder standing between the closet and the wall. It was always kept there, but now it looked like someone had used it and put it back in a hurry.

*It can't be that our ninety-year-old neighbor climbed up that ladder to hide the afikoman!* I said to myself. *Isn't there a limit to how far he would go, no matter how important it is to him?*

After another round of searching, I decided that just to be on the safe side I'd check the top of that closet.

I climbed up the ladder, reached into the small space between the closet and the ceiling—and touched the *afikoman* bag.

Was I impressed! At his age, Reb Henich really deserved credit for making that kind of physical effort.

Most likely my satisfaction in discovering the hiding place made me feel generous enough to give him credit.

I went back to the table. On the way, I made another decision. I wouldn't tell anyone that I'd found the *afikoman*. I'd save it as a surprise for the end.

I hid the *afikoman* under my shirt and returned to the table with a mournful expression.

"*Nu?* Did you find it?" everyone asked.

"Don't worry. You'll have the *afikoman* by *Tzafun*."

I had chosen my words carefully. I hadn't lied, but I'd led them to believe that I hadn't found the *afikoman* and that it was hard for me to admit defeat.

It worked. My brothers and sisters said things like "Just admit that you didn't find it" and "Look how red your face is."

"You'll see," is all I replied, as if I myself didn't believe what I was saying. If you had been there, you would have thought not only that I did not find the *afikoman* but that I was a great actor.

The Seder continued, and you've never seen me read the Haggadah with such enthusiasm. I read it aloud and sang all the songs. I was totally involved, just like *Chazal* wanted when they instituted the custom of hiding the *afikoman*.

The meal began, and the food was delicious. Unlike the previous year, when I barely ate and fell asleep in the middle, this year I was wide awake. Even if I'd wanted to, I couldn't have fallen asleep for a minute. I was waiting for that peak moment when I'd show everyone that I really *had* found the *afikoman*.

*   *   *

*Shulchan Orech* ended, and it was time for *Tzafun*.

"Did anyone find my *afikoman*?" my father asked.

I went over to the bookcase and took out the *afikoman* that I'd found right after he'd hidden it. I gave it to my father with a big smile, trying hard not to look smug.

"What do you want in exchange?" my father asked.

I asked for a CD player for me and my brother. We all knew we would have gotten it anyway.

Now it was Reb Henich's turn.

"You didn't find it this year, did you?" he said to me. "Of course. I hid it well. That's why you didn't find it."

Everyone looked at me, but I was completely calm.

"Please, let's see the *afikoman*," I said. (I knew that he'd go to the children's room and climb the ladder again, only to discover that someone had gotten there first. And that someone was me.)

Reb Henich stood up, but instead of going to the children's room, he said, "I really fooled you this year. I went everywhere in the house, but I didn't put down the *afikoman*! I hid it in my *kittel*."

Before I could utter a peep, he put his hand into his *kittel* and took out a bag with the word *afikoman* embroidered on it.

While everyone else smiled and congratulated him, I felt like I was going to pass out.

I didn't dare say it, but I knew that the elderly Reb Henich wasn't telling the truth.

I wanted to shout it out, but I decided not to. As angry as I felt, I knew that if I pulled out the real *afikoman*, Reb Henich would be humiliated—and I wasn't willing to humiliate someone in public for all the money in the world.

I felt the room spinning around me. I stood up, ran to my room, flung myself on my bed, and started sobbing.

My parents followed me. My mother hugged me and said, "What happened, Binyamin? You were so wonderful all through the Seder even though you knew you hadn't found the *afikoman*. What happened all of a sudden?"

I just kept on crying.

My father started to get angry, but my mother said to him, "I sense that something else is going on here. I know Binyamin. Something happened, didn't it?" she asked me.

I lifted my head. "Yes."

"What happened?"

"I can't say."

My father sat down next to me and said in his special voice that was both gentle yet authoritative,

"Binyamin, we're your parents and we want only your good. Tell us right now why you're acting like this. I noticed a sudden change of expression on your face. What happened, Binyamin?"

I knew that there are no secrets from parents, and that I was allowed to tell them. "Abba, Ima," I said through my tears, "I *did* find the *afikoman* that Reb Henich hid. I don't know what he took out of his *kittel*."

My parents looked at me in disbelief. "What do you mean you found it? We saw Reb Henich take it out of the *afikoman* bag. Everyone at the table saw it. You saw it, too, didn't you?"

"Sure, but what Reb Henich took out wasn't the *afikoman*."

To my parents' astonishment, I pulled out the *afikoman* I'd been hiding under my shirt. "*This* is the *afikoman*! I found it here in this room, up there on top of the closet."

My parents stared at the satin bag and didn't know what to make of it.

My father was the first to recover. "Reb Henich is a big *talmid chacham*," he said. "He would never lie. Maybe…maybe he forgot. Or it's possible that…" He fell silent. Even my father couldn't think of anything to say.

My parents left the room to talk it over. They came to a decision.

My father invited Reb Henich to join him in another room, and they closed the door behind them. I waited outside. In the living room everyone was still waiting and had no idea what had happened.

The conversation between my father and our guest lasted a few minutes. Then the door opened, Reb Henich took my hand, and said, "Come with me to the Seder table."

He led me to the head of the table and then started to speak.

"Look at this mystery," he said. "As you all saw, I announced that the *afikoman* was in my *kittel*, and I even showed it to you. But sitting right there in front of me was a wonderful boy who had inside his shirt something that completely contradicted what I was saying."

Reb Henich looked at me and said, "Show everyone what you had inside your shirt."

I hesitated, but because our elderly guest asked me to, I did it. I showed everyone the bag in my hand.

Murmurs of surprise rippled around the table.

"Before I explain what happened here," Reb Henich said, "I want to praise Binyamin, who, despite the shock I gave him when he thought I was lying, made the choice to hide it from all of you so as not to embarrass me. You don't see that kind of behavior in every child. For that alone, he deserves a rich reward in heaven…and down here on earth as well.

"Now I'd like to tell you, and him, what really happened. Listen carefully…"

I told you I like mysteries. I'm positive that now you do, too. How would the guest explain what happened?

\*   \*   \*

"Once, about a year ago, I was young," Reb Henich began with a chuckle. We all laughed. "I had more energy, or at least I thought I did, and I decided to hide the *afikoman* in a place where no one would think of looking for it.

"As you will remember, I went through all the rooms, and that fooled you. What you didn't know was that when I got to the children's room, I took the ladder, climbed up just as I used to sixty years ago, and put the *afikoman* in that small space between the top of the closet and the ceiling.

"As you remember from last year, Binyamin, my main challenger," he said with a wink as everyone laughed, "gave up and went to sleep, which made me lose all interest in the *afikoman*. After all, who was the whole ceremony for if not him?

"When the time came to eat the *afikoman*, I said to myself that I wasn't going to risk life and limb to climb up on that ladder again, especially since Binyamin wasn't around. I fulfilled my obligation with Binyamin's father's *afikoman*. I planned to tell him after the holiday to retrieve the *afikoman* from the top of the closet, but it slipped my mind.

"Binyamin, what you found is last year's *afikoman*, and you deserve the biggest reward in the world for it. You had every good reason to tell everyone the truth, but the *chinuch* you received from your parents and your good *middos* stopped you. Anything you could possibly ask for would not equal in value what you did by keeping quiet. You controlled yourself, though you were upset and angry, and you didn't tell anyone what you thought I had done. And all because you didn't want to embarrass me in front of others. For that you will receive immeasurable reward in the next world."

That's the story. This year, I'll be twelve and a half at Pesach, almost bar mitzvah. I think I'll leave the *afikoman* search to my younger brother, Reuven, who's ten.

Besides, you and I know that last year I got the biggest reward I could ever get for an *afikoman*, and I always like to quit while I'm ahead.

# Social Challenge

**My name is Yehuda.**

I'm twelve, and I'm in the sixth grade.

I'm a kid with a lot of energy. I like to play and talk with friends, and I'm pretty good in school, too.

The only thing is, ever since I can remember, I've had problems with other kids. It's not that I bother them. It's that *they* bother *me*. They call me names, laugh at me, and tease me. They do anything and everything to torment me.

Ever since the first grade, I've come home from school with at least one story of someone picking on me. I've already stopped counting the times kids picked on me over the years. What didn't I do to try to stop them! I complained to the teacher, my parents talked to the principal, I tried to talk to the kids myself. Not only didn't that help, it made things worse, because they'd laugh at me and imitate my pleading.

I realized that going to the teacher didn't accomplish anything, so I started to fight back. When I did that, one of two things happened. Either the boy I'd give it back to would tattle to the teacher and the teacher would punish me. Or the boy would get a few of his friends to jump on me.

Nothing I tried worked.

It's hard for me to describe what I went through during those years. Try to imagine a wound on your hand, and someone comes every day and gives it a bang and it opens up again and again. It never gets a chance to heal because it's never given a chance.

*   *   *

One day, after school let out, I found myself running down the street with about half the class chasing after me.

How did I get into such a situation? Don't ask. Actually, you already know the answer.

Someone said something, I got mad and said something back, he shouted to everyone, and of course they took his side.

And that's how, to my shame, I was forced to run away with half the class running after me and shouting taunts. They had one aim and one aim only, and it was

pretty obvious: to catch me and let out their anger on me.

Passersby saw a scene you don't see every day. But not a single one of them thought to intervene.

And then I saw in front of me an old man with a cane. He was standing right where the path gets narrow, where only one person can squeeze by.

I knew that if I kept running I'd have to push him aside, but if I stopped running they'd catch me.

I chose the second option. I stopped.

\*   \*   \*

They all surrounded me, their eyes blazing with fury. A few hands found their way to my head, and I knew what was coming next.

Suddenly a voice thundered, "Stop!"

It was the old man, who knew that they'd only caught me because I'd stopped for him.

They ignored him, and one of the boys, Nachum, hissed, "Mind your own business."

"I'm going to tell your father how chutzpadik you are!" the old man shouted, and he mentioned the name of Nachum's father.

That was pretty convincing, because it's one thing for a kid to be fresh but another thing for his father to know he was fresh—and to an old person, no less. An old person who knew his father by name, too.

"All of you—get out of here!" the old man shouted. "Otherwise I'm going straight to your principal, Rabbi Cohen. I'll take him on a tour of your classroom and identify each and every one of you."

The thought of the principal knowing what they had done was even more frightening than Nachum's father finding out. Everyone ran away. Only I remained standing there.

"What's your name?" the old man asked me.

"Yehuda," I answered.

"Yehuda what?"

I told him my family name.

"Oh, you're the son of Reb So-and-so." And here he said my father's name.

"Yes."

"Your father is an *avrech chashuv*. I know him well."

I walked alongside him until we came to a bench that usually old people sat on.

"Sit down, my child," he said. "I want to talk to you."

I didn't really want to sit next to an old man, on a bench for old people. But I sat down for the same reason I stopped running. I respect my elders.

"What's going on with you?" he asked me. "How did you manage to get all the kids in your class chasing after you to beat you up?"

"Only half," I mumbled.

"Sorry, only half," he repeated, but I knew he wasn't really sorry.

I didn't say anything.

"I have a reason for asking," he said. "I think I can help you."

Sure he could help me! Fat chance. That's all I needed, was for him to come to school to identify the troublemakers. After that, the other half of the class would be running after me, too.

"Don't worry. I'm not going to your principal, Rabbi Cohen," he said as if reading my mind. "Just tell me one thing. Who started it?"

"They hurt my feelings," I said.

"How?"

"They called me names."

"How did you react?"

"I got mad."

"People have probably told you not to get angry when this happens."

"They have."

"And...?"

"And I can't help it. I get angry."

"They probably told you that even if you do get angry, you should at least not show it," the elderly man said.

"That's what they always tell me," I said. "And even without them telling me, I know that by myself."

"So…?"

"I try to hold it in, but I can't. It's like someone is putting a burning hot iron on me and I'm supposed to stop myself from shouting that it hurts. They hurt me, they humiliate me to my face, they embarrass me — how can I not react?"

"I understand you completely," the old man said. "Unlike everyone else, I truly understand."

We sat there in silence. After a moment he said, "What if I give you a trick, a way to react without them knowing you're reacting?"

"There's no such thing," I said. "Everyone reacts on purpose so that they'll know he's reacting."

"Do you agree that I'm several years older than you?" he asked with a smile.

I looked at him. He looked to be around eighty years old. "I would say that you are older than I am by about sixty-eight years."

"Excellent," he said. "Then you most probably

realize that I could tell you a few things you might not know."

"Agreed."

"I want to tell you a story."

I certainly wasn't going to refuse to listen to a story.

*   *   *

This is a story about my father (the old man told me), may he rest in peace, who was a very big *talmid chacham*. He was born in Lithuania more than a hundred years ago, and even as a child he was an outstanding student. After his bar mitzvah, he traveled to learn in Toras Chesed, which everyone called Yeshivas Brisk, led by Hagaon Harav Yitzchak Zev Halevi Soloveichik, *ztz"l*. There he sat and learned with great *hasmadah* for years.

Many of the greatest *talmidim* in Lithuania learned in Brisk, which means they were some of the greatest *lamdanim* in the whole world. Clothing didn't matter to them, nor did food or anything material, only learning Torah from morning to night.

One day, a boy of eleven arrived at the yeshivah. At first they thought he was the son of one of the *roshei yeshivah* and he had only come there to talk to his father. Then they saw him being given a room and a bed, and he sat down to learn in the *beis medrash*. The only thing they could find out about him was that his name was Aharon Leib and that he was eleven.

His presence irritated a lot of the *bachurim*, because they felt their honor was diminished by having such a young boy come to learn in their yeshivah that was famous throughout the Jewish world. They decided that if he came over to ask them a question, they'd ignore him.

But they never got a chance to ignore him. A day passed and then another, and Aharon never came to ask them any questions. All day long he sat in front of his Gemara, not lifting his eyes from the page. He didn't pay any attention to what was going on around him.

After a week during which they were unsuccessful in showing the boy that they were ignoring him, they tried to come up with another way to let him know that his presence wasn't wanted. Then someone had an idea.

"Let's put a toy on his bed. Maybe then he'll get the hint that he belongs with other children and not here in the most illustrious yeshivah in the world."

My father was the one chosen to put the toy on his bed. Or, to be more exact, a stuffed animal that one of the *bachurim* had found in the trash—worthless, but good enough to give the message.

My father put the toy on the boy's bed, and they waited patiently. They figured that when nighttime came and he saw the stuffed animal on his bed, he'd go complain to the *rabbeim*. The *rabbeim* would talk to the *bachurim*, and the answer they'd give was that a child like that didn't belong in their yeshivah.

Their plan didn't work. Night came and went. In the morning, when they all went to the *beis medrash* to daven, they were surprised to see young Aharon bent over his Gemara, which meant he'd gotten up to learn before davening.

If they'd hoped that he'd go to the *rabbeim* after davening, they quickly discovered how wrong they were. The boy sat and learned diligently as if nothing had happened.

The *bachurim* sent my father to Aharon's room, or to be more accurate, to the small cubbyhole under the stairs that served as his sleeping corner. To their astonishment, they discovered that the bed was made, the covers perfectly smooth and straight. Sitting there on top, exactly where they'd left it, was the stuffed animal.

"He must have slept somewhere else last night," they reasoned. "We'll wait for tonight."

One of the *bachurim* stayed in the *beis medrash* to find out when the boy went to sleep. Midnight came, then one o'clock, and the boy was still poring over his Gemara. At two o'clock, the *bachur* who was watching him gave up and went to sleep.

The next day, two *bachurim* went to the boy's room and found the stuffed animal in exactly the same spot where they had left it.

Only then did they realize that this boy never went to sleep. He literally learned day and night.

Some of them still weren't convinced, but when another week went by with the stuffed animal still in its place, the *alter bachur* (the oldest boy in the yeshivah) went over to the eleven-year-old and invited him to be his *chavrusa*.

Naturally, the boy was happy to agree, and the two started to learn together. What a commotion that raised in the yeshivah! And in all of Brisk, for that matter. Everyone realize that this boy was no ordinary boy but a genius who was destined for greatness in Torah.

And with that, the matter ended.

* * *

Years passed, and the Holocaust arrived. My father suffered greatly but survived. When it was over, he traveled to the United States, married, and began learning in a yeshivah. All of his children, myself included, learned in yeshivah and became Torah scholars. I was sent to learn in Yeshivas Brisk in Yerushalayim, and there is where I married and settled.

More years passed, and the boy's name began to be heard, first as *rosh yeshivah* of the *yeshivah ketanah* of Ponevezh, then as *rosh yeshivah* of Yeshivas Gaon Yaakov and *rosh yeshivah* of Yeshivas Orchos Torah.

Now he was recognized as one of the *gedolei hador* alongside Harav Yosef Shalom Elyashiv, *ztz"l*.

\* \* \*

Ten years ago, my father came from the States to visit me. He was ninety-nine years old, but as mentally alert as a young man. He stayed in my home, and that's when he told me this story for the first time. He said he wanted to go to the home of Harav Aharon Leib Steinman, *shlita*, to ask his forgiveness for the prank he'd pulled when he was a *bachur*.

I told him that I didn't think there was any harm done, because the boy hadn't gone to sleep and never even saw the stuffed animal. But my father insisted that he wanted to ask forgiveness, because even if the boy hadn't felt hurt, the very fact that he had wanted to hurt the boy obligated him to beg his forgiveness.

I willingly fulfilled my father's command, and the very next day we got up before dawn to daven with the minyan in Rav Steinman's home. After davening, my father introduced himself as someone who had learned in Brisk with Rav Steinman. Rav Steinman recognized him and greeted him warmly, showing him great honor. Not only that, but he began talking in learning with my father about the *sugya* the yeshivah had been learning when they were there. I was awed and amazed at how sharp his memory was despite the many years that had passed.

Then my father said with some embarrassment that he'd come to ask the Rosh Yeshivah to please forgive him.

"For what?" the Rosh Yeshivah asked him in wonder.

My father told the Rosh Yeshivah about the *bachurim's* anger at his acceptance into the yeshivah as a child of only eleven, about the stuffed animal that he himself had placed on his bed, and about the moment they realized that he had stayed up sitting and learning and hadn't gone to sleep. That was when they had changed their attitude toward him and become his admirers.

Rav Steinman smiled and even laughed. He said that though he didn't remember a thing about it, he completely forgave my father. He also emphasized that it wasn't possible for him not to have slept.

"True, it was a time when I was deeply immersed in learning," he said, "but my father had instructed me to get at least three hours of sleep every night. I did go to sleep late, but I made sure to get the minimum amount of sleep that would allow me to sit and learn."

"If so," said my father, "the Rav probably didn't notice the stuffed animal, because I remember like yesterday how I saw it there on the bed, day after day, for a whole week."

"Most likely," the Rosh Yeshivah said. "And if so, there was no offense taken. In any event, I forgive you completely as well as the others, and bless both you and your son with long lives."

They parted in strong friendship, with the Rosh Yeshivah accompanying us to the building's stairs outside his apartment, an honor reserved for the greatest Torah scholars.

\*　　\*　　\*

My father was very moved by the meeting and didn't say a word all the way home. When we got back to my house, he sat down in an armchair and burst into bitter tears.

I gave him his privacy until he calmed down, and then he asked me to listen to what he had to say.

"You know, I turned it over this way and that, and suddenly I understood everything. Anyone who observes the Rosh Yeshivah knows that as great as his humility is, that's how smart he is. The more I think about it, the more I've come to realize what must have happened. The boy Aharon must have reached his bed at two thirty or three in the morning, seen the stuffed animal, moved it aside to go to sleep, and in the morning put it back in its place. He must have realized that someone was trying to tease him, and he knew that the best way to handle it was to act as if nothing had happened.

"How mistaken we were! We never imagined he was that clever. The only conclusion that came to our minds was that he had never gone to sleep. The possibility that this young child was so wise that he understood that the only way to deal with that kind of teasing is to ignore it didn't even occur to us.

"If everyone were that wise and so able to restrain himself, our world would look a lot better, without all the fighting over meaningless things."

Here the old man ended his story, and I saw that he was very emotional.

"Do you understand why I told you that story?" he asked me.

"I think so."

"Try to explain it to me."

"That if I don't answer back or respond, they'll leave me alone."

"Yes, but the main point of the story is missing. It's not enough that you don't respond. You *yourself* need to ignore it, not to pay any attention to it, or at least to act as if you're not hurt at all. Because if they see that you notice or even get mad inside, they'll keep doing it. Only if you show that it really doesn't affect you will the bullying stop. It won't take more than a day, but I promise you that if you act as the *gadol hador* did when he was your age, you'll get the same results."

\* \* \*

I left that conversation a different boy.

From that day on, I didn't react to any teasing or bullying. When someone called me a name (which used to cause most of the fights), I'd answer, "Yes? What did you want?" as if the nickname was my real name. For a while, a few of them tried to test me to see if maybe

I'd get mad. But that never happened. I decided that even if the nickname stuck to me till the end of my life, I wouldn't get upset.

Guess what? As soon as they saw that the nickname didn't hurt my feelings, they stopped using it. And when they saw that nothing irritated me, they slowly but surely stopped bothering me. Without my even noticing it, kids started being friendly to me.

The year ended without a trace of any of the difficulties I'd been through in other years.

\*    \*    \*

That's my story. Take it as a present to all kids who are bullied. Don't pay any attention. Don't get mad. Learn from the *gadol hador* Harav Aharon Leib Steinman, *shlita*, who ignored the stuffed animal placed on his bed to tease him when he was only a boy of eleven.

Sometimes I wonder what would have happened if he had gotten upset and started to cry and point a finger of blame, like we all do. Who knows what a loss that would have been to the entire Jewish world?

# (Not So) Private Tutor

**My name is Chaim.**

I live in Ashdod, and I'm in the sixth grade.

I'm a popular kid. I'm also a good student, and the teachers in school like me, though I have to admit I get into trouble once in a while. I can't complain, because I deserved whatever punishments I've gotten.

I think my story will be cause for discussion among kids—and even parents. I myself still haven't decided what to think about it. Which means that sometimes I think one way about it and sometimes another.

Instead of keeping you in suspense, I'll just go ahead and tell you what happened to me. Then you can decide for yourself what to make of it.

\*   \*   \*

It all began during recess one day. I was walking in the classroom and tripped over a backpack in the aisle.

The backpack fell over, and everything in it spilled out onto the floor.

I bent down to put everything back. The labels told me it was the backpack of my classmate Naftali.

Naftali was one of the best students in the class. He was on top of the material, he listened in class and never disturbed, and he was also an active participant in class. Some might say too active, because every time the teacher asked a question, he was the first to raise his hand. Sometimes it seemed like he was trying to show off how smart he was.

On the other hand, he did try to help other kids. If a boy had a question on the material we were learning or got stuck on homework, Naftali would take the time to help him.

As I was returning items to his backpack, I was seeing Naftali's organized notebooks and neat handwriting for the very first time. As you might have guessed, a few notebooks happened to fall open—by themselves, of course.

And then I picked up his planner.

I myself don't write down everything in my planner, and even when I do, it's half a word here or some kind of code like "HW grammar. Trip 2 days. Parents sign." Stuff like that, written on the fly. Lots of times even I

forget what it means. Like what exactly do my parents need to sign?

Naftali's planner, though, was neat, clean, and organized. Every day was filled in. He wrote down what we had learned in each subject, all the homework assignments, projects due, and things to remember. It was a pleasure to read. I remembered that any time anyone in class wanted information, whether about homework or a past event, he'd ask Naftali, who would look in his planner and give him an answer.

Today I know that it's totally wrong to go through someone's personal items and read what he's written. I also know about the *cherem* of Rabbeinu Gershom against someone who reads other people's papers (and maybe I knew about it even then…). But at the time, standing there with the open planner in my hands, I couldn't resist the temptation.

I read it.

All of a sudden, my eyes caught one item that repeated itself. In the spaces for Tuesday and Thursday, at exactly six o'clock, was written: "Private tutor."

I flipped back to the previous weeks and months, and discovered that the same entry appeared since the beginning of the year. Every Tuesday and Thursday, Naftali went to a private tutor.

*Aha!* I said to myself. *Now I know Naftali's secret—why he is so good in school. He's got a private tutor! That's not fair.*

I finished returning all the notebooks and books to the backpack and ran out to play. But I didn't just play.

What do you think I did after looking at my friend's planner without his permission? I went and told *everyone* what I'd seen. A group gathered around me, and I told them excitedly that Naftali wasn't such a great student. The proof? He had a private tutor.

Near the end of the break, my friend Shlomo suggested that we follow Naftali to see where he went after school. We'd show him that we all knew he was going to a private tutor, so he shouldn't be so stuck up.

You can add this to the list of all the bad things I did that day. Besides disobeying the *cherem* of Rabbeinu Gershom and speaking *lashon hara* and *rechilus*, now I was about to embarrass someone in public.

In my defense, let me just say that I didn't do it to be mean. I acted without thinking. That doesn't mean I'm not ashamed of what I did, because I am. Very. I'm only writing it so that other kids will make sure not to do the same thing.

\* \* \*

The next day was Tuesday. After school let out, we followed Naftali. We were eight kids walking down the sidewalk, but we'd split up into two groups so we'd be on opposite sides of the street. With four of us on one side and four on the other, we didn't attract any attention.

Naftali didn't suspect a thing, until he reached a certain building. We followed him into the lobby and shouted, "Hold it!" He jumped and spun around.

"The game is up," we told him. "We know that you're going to a private tutor."

Naftali looked scared. He hadn't expected eight boys to surprise him like that.

"So what?" he said. "It's nothing to be ashamed of."

"What a joke," one of the boys said. "You pretend to be the best student in class, but we found out the truth. You're really lazy."

Naftali tried to argue, but then he caught on that we hadn't followed him to talk to him but to laugh at him. When he realized that, he started to cry. "You should be ashamed of yourselves!" he shouted. "What did I ever do to you? I'll never forgive you!"

He had a point. A good point. I started to feel bad, but I didn't know what I was supposed to do about it.

All of a sudden, a man appeared. "What's going on here?"

"Are you his private tutor?" Yochanan asked. He's got a big mouth.

The man looked at us. "Who's asking?"

"We are. His classmates. We followed Naftali here and found out that he goes to a private tutor, so he shouldn't pretend that he's the best student in class."

The man's expression turned serious. "Do you mean to tell me that you all came here to find out if he goes to a private tutor? You wanted to humiliate him in public?"

We didn't answer. Yochanan opened his mouth to say something, but the expression on the man's face silenced him.

The man looked at each one of us in turn. It seemed that he was trying to come to a decision.

"I want to tell you," he said, "that I have never encountered such meanness and cruelty. But what I find most irritating is that there are another two children here who also come to me for tutoring, and now they're pretending that they don't. I really can't understand it."

He looked at each of us in turn. Suddenly the spotlight wasn't on Naftali anymore. We all wanted to

know which one of us also went to a private tutor yet still joined the group that had come to laugh at Naftali.

"We don't believe it," I said. "You're just saying that. Tell us who they are."

"I'm not sure they'd want me to," the tutor said. "I'd need to ask a boy's permission before telling people that I'm his private tutor. Would *you* agree to let me tell everyone that I give *you* private lessons?"

"Yes!" I shouted. "You have my permission. If I come to you for lessons, I have no problem with you saying it."

"Wait just one minute," the tutor said. He whipped out his cell phone, scrolled down the names, pressed Call, and stepped away so that we couldn't overhear the conversation.

It was strange. We didn't know if the call he was making was related to what we'd just been talking about or whether he'd suddenly remembered he had a call to make.

He ended the call and came back to where we were standing.

"So, what do you say? None of you have any problem with me telling the others that I'm your private tutor?"

"None at all," I said confidently.

"Okay," the tutor said. "You're first."

Everyone looked at me.

"He's just saying that," I said. "He's just saying things to defend Naftali. It's not true."

"Really?" the man said. "Then take a look at this." He took his wallet out of his pocket, opened it, and pulled out a check.

It was my father's check. Made out for three hundred shekels.

"Would you like to ask your father to come here to prove that it's his?" the tutor asked.

I was shocked. I couldn't believe this was happening to me. Everyone looked at me with scorn, and I started to cry.

I turned around and ran out as fast as I could. I ran because of the humiliation, but even more because I knew that the tutor wasn't telling the truth.

I'd never gone to him for private lessons. I'd never even met him before.

*   *   *

I was still crying when I got home. My mother was there, and she listened to me patiently. I told her what had happened to me with the tutor, how he'd lied to my face, saying that I went to him for lessons, humiliating me in front of my friends. She listened to me and didn't say anything. She dried my tears and calmed me down.

I saw that she was upset. I know my mother. She was worried about me, but I sensed that she was also angry at me and was just waiting for me to calm down.

I calmed down and then we talked.

"Tell me something," my mother said to me in a tone of voice reserved for a certain type of questioning, "how did you know that this boy was going to a private tutor?"

I told her.

She was appalled. "Do you mean to tell me that you invaded the privacy of a boy in your class?"

"Yes," I said. "I'm sorry."

"How did everyone else find out about it?" she asked me (even though she probably knew the answer to that question herself).

"I told them."

"You *told* them?" she exclaimed in disbelief. "You invaded your friend's privacy and then you gossiped about him in a way that looks very much like *lashon hara*?"

"Yes," I admitted.

"How did you get to the tutor's house?"

"One of the boys had the idea that we should follow him and see who his tutor is."

"'One of the boys,'" my mother echoed. "Do you think that was a good idea or a bad one?"

"Not good."

"Yet you went along with this idea," my mother said. "What happened when you got there? What did you do? Did you just look, or did you say something? I don't think the tutor would just appear out of nowhere."

I caught on to the direction in which she was heading, and at that moment I was really sorry I'd told her.

"We laughed at him," I said. "We told him that he pretends to be the smartest kid in the class, but now we found out that he's going to a tutor."

"So you're saying that you joined in humiliating a boy in public. Is that what you're saying?"

"Yes," I answered. All of a sudden, it dawned on me exactly what I'd done.

"And you still have complaints," my mother asked, "about the big crime that was done to *you*?"

I gave that some thought. Even though I realized what a low level I'd sunk to, I still felt that my mother wasn't appreciating the injustice done to me. The tutor had told an outright lie to hurt me. That was wrong. Sure, I knew I hadn't acted right, but was doing something like that to a kid the right way for a tutor to act?

I told my mother how I felt. I said it quietly and hesitantly, but in our house we say everything. We don't hide things.

My mother told me that she also found it puzzling, but she judged the tutor favorably and assumed he was trying to protect his student at any cost.

"At my expense?" I asked.

As soon as the words were out of my mouth, I knew the answer.

"Particularly at your expense. You're the last person who has any say in the matter. I still have some reservations about what the tutor did, I must say, but you have no right to talk. I hope you realize that I'm going to tell your father everything. He'll decide what you need to do now. You know that we've taught you not to wrong others, yet that's exactly what you did."

When my father came home, I went to my room. I knew that my mother would tell him everything. I almost asked her not to, but I didn't. Something inside me wanted my father to help me out of the trouble I'd gotten myself into.

There was another reason, too. I wanted my father

to know what the tutor had done. It was important to me that he take care of it. I knew he wouldn't let it go by. The lie still bothered me.

*　*　*

An hour later, my parents came into my room.

"I'm very surprised and dismayed at what happened today," my father said. "Yes, one sin leads to another, and what you did today is a perfect example of that. I don't know how my son, whom I raised to show caring and sensitivity to others, could do such a thing. You'll need to atone for such deeds, not as punishment, but as a privilege."

I hung my head in shame. Though it wasn't easy for me to hear it, I knew that those words were spoken with love and with my benefit in mind.

"I also heard what the tutor said to you in front of everyone. I know you. Your sense of justice, which seems to have been asleep today, suddenly woke up when you were the victim. Am I right?"

I nodded. That was my father. He knew how to say hard things in a way that made them easy to take.

"Well, I have news for you," my father said. "Do you remember that the tutor made a phone call before saying what he did?"

"Yes," I said, surprised. "But how do *you* know?"

"Because he called me," my father said. "He told me briefly what had happened, and I was the one who gave him permission to reveal that I had paid him to teach you."

My jaw dropped.

"His name is Rabbi Gold," my father said. "For your information, I arranged for him to give you private lessons, beginning next week. Not because you're lazy or having a hard time. It's just that I want you to grow in Torah, and Rabbi Gold is an *avrech* who will help you love learning. I paid him in advance for the first month, and I was about to tell you about it when this happened.

"I must admit, though, that if it hadn't been true, I would have taken him to task for it. Yet I admire the extent to which he's willing to go to protect a student. At least you know that Rabbi Gold is the type of tutor who will do anything to protect you…"

My father fell silent, and I waited for what I knew was coming next.

But he didn't say anything more.

"What about my punishment?" I asked when I couldn't take the suspense any longer.

My father gave a tight smile. "I'm glad you realize

that you deserve one. But didn't I give you your punishment already when I gave Rabbi Gold permission to reveal that he is your private tutor? Actually, I didn't do that as a punishment but to prevent you from a much greater punishment."

I looked at him in astonishment. My mother did, too.

"Do you know what the punishment is for someone who shames another person in public?" my father asked. "They say there is no end to his punishment. I can tell you that I personally have seen that everyone who has humiliated or tormented another person, or made his life miserable in any way, eventually paid a terrible price for it. You can just imagine the pain and anguish that might have come your way for the terrible thing you did. I acted like a father who saw his son standing in the middle of the street with a bus barreling toward him. I pushed him out of the way. He might have gotten bruised, but he was saved from being run over.

"You experienced some shame—not too much, but just enough to prevent you from getting the far more serious punishment given to someone who embarrasses another person in public.

"So you've already gotten your punishment," my

father said, summing it up. "What will happen is that tomorrow you'll go to school and apologize to Naftali in front of the whole class. You'll tell your classmates that your father arranged for Rabbi Gold to tutor you without your knowledge, and that you're going to start learning with him the next day.

"It will be pretty uncomfortable, but you deserve it. Explain to everyone that you got carried away and made a mistake. Apologize. You'll have a few days' discomfort, but you'll get through it."

*   *   *

Believe it or not, I did it. I needed a lot of support from my parents during those next few days. I was really scared of my friends' reactions, but I knew it was the right thing to do.

The next day I apologized to Naftali. I told my friends that I would be taking lessons from the tutor, and that I don't know what made me torment Naftali like that. During recess I talked with Naftali for a long time. I explained everything that had happened, and I asked him to forgive me with his whole heart.

He forgave me. And guess what? Naftali had no problem with people knowing he was going to a private tutor. He'd never thought to hide it, so our following him made him feel embarrassed and uncomfortable for nothing. My revelation that I, too, would be going to the very same tutor repaired the damage totally.

\* \* \*

I've been going to Rabbi Gold, the private tutor, twice a week ever since. Every Shabbos I learn with Naftali *b'chavrusa*, and the fact that we know how to learn benefits us both a lot. We've become friends.

Now I know that having a private tutor is nothing to be ashamed of. My sister also goes to a private tutor and doesn't hide it from anyone.

But the biggest lesson I learned from the tutor was the one I got even before I knew him — and that lesson is one (I hope) I'll never, ever forget.

# Library Thriller

**My name is Tamar.**

I'm eleven, and I live in Modi'in Illit.

I've got tons of friends, do well in school, and the main thing is, I like to read.

My story begins from when I was two. Don't worry. I'm not going to bore you with toddler tales. But it's important for what I want to tell you.

From the time we kids were very young, my father taught us a very important skill. Maybe if you tell your parents about it, they'll do the same.

Because of all the tragedies of young children being left inside a car and not being able to get out, from the minute one of us kids knew how to walk, my father taught us how to get out of the car by ourselves.

You're probably wondering how.

Though so many years have passed since then, I vaguely remember how he taught me, but mostly I think I remember it because I've watched him teach my younger brothers and sisters.

It works like this:

My father buys a big present and says to the kid, "Today we're going to play a game. I'm going to put you in the car and show you how to open the seatbelt, get out of the car seat, go to the car door, release the lock, and open the door."

Actually, the child doesn't really understand what my father is saying because it's all too complicated for a two-year-old. But he does understand what happens next. My father puts him in the car, sits him in the car seat, and buckles the harness with a click. Then he says, "Try to get out."

At first it's hard, but after a few tries, the child manages to unbuckle the harness. His accomplishment is rewarded by a round of applause from the rest of the family.

Next, the kid gets out of the car seat and goes to the locked car door. My father shows him which button to push. At that age, it's not easy. But, like I said, all it takes is practice. When the child pushes the button and opens the door, he gets another round of enthusiastic applause.

After these "lessons" comes the test.

My father puts the child in the car seat, buckles the harness, gets out of the car, and locks it.

From outside the car, he shouts to the child, "Now get out of the seat, go to the door, and open it."

It usually takes a few tries, because at first the child doesn't know what he's supposed to do. But in the end, he does manage to get out of the car seat and open the door. His reward is the big prize.

That's how we all learned how to get out of a locked car, not that we ever needed it. My father *never, ever* forgot us in the car.

Now I can tell you my story, because it's connected to what I just told you. As I wrote before, I really, really like to read. And that means I have a library card for four libraries. The only problem is that it takes me only two days to finish reading all the books I take out. That's why I spend hours sitting in the school library, where I can read to my heart's content.

It happened one Thursday. I was sitting and reading in my usual corner. My "usual corner" is in the back of the library, where it's the quietest. There I can read as much as I want, without anyone bothering me.

I was deeply engrossed in a book and had been reading for hours. When I reached the last page, I looked up and saw that the lights were off. I could still read, because there was an emergency light above me, but the whole library was dark.

I thought maybe there was an electricity blackout, but another thing that caught my attention was the quiet. My corner was always quiet, but I could usually hear whispers from other girls and the sound of the librarians talking. Now it was absolutely quiet.

I got up to see what was going on. When I got to the librarians' desk, I saw that no one was there. I thought that maybe the librarian had gone out for a minute, so I went to the exit, and that's when I discovered that the library was locked.

The school library is in a bomb shelter, so when I say locked, I'm talking about the heavy steel door to the shelter that is locked and bolted from the outside.

They had forgotten me inside the library.

\* \* \*

I started banging on the door. I knocked and banged for a few minutes, but I didn't hear anything in response.

The library isn't in the main school building, but at the far end of the schoolyard. I'll try to describe it better so you'll understand what a mess I was in.

At the end of the schoolyard, there's a bomb shelter

with a metal door. When that door is open, you can go down one flight of stairs. At the bottom is another metal door. That's the one I was banging on.

Which means that even if anyone *was* in the schoolyard, she wouldn't hear me, because I was locked in by two steel doors.

*Uh-oh*, I thought. *I might get stuck down here all night. Alone. In the library.*

I started to cry. I don't know for how long. I think I must have cried until I didn't have the strength to cry anymore.

Then I sat there and started to think about my situation. That's when I realized that things were much scarier than I'd thought.

*Today is Thursday*, I thought to myself. *Tomorrow is Friday, and the library is closed. Except for a short recess, the girls won't be outside in the yard. Even if they do go out to play, it will be so noisy they won't hear my bangs. Which means that I could be stuck here over Shabbos, and I'll only be able to get out on Sunday morning.*

You have no idea how scared I was right then.

Thoughts raced through my mind, and I had no control over them. Fear, terror, wanting to cry. I couldn't even think straight.

I thought about my parents, who were probably

worried about me. Would they know I was in the library?

Not a chance. That day I'd come home from school and told my mother that I was going to my friend Gila's house. I really did go to Gila, but she wasn't home, so I went to the library instead.

I knew my parents would start looking for me, but would it occur to them that I was in the library? They'd probably think that I had disappeared, that someone had kidnapped me.

I thought about how worried they'd be and, no less than that, how the whole country would search for me, while I was trapped here in the library.

\*   \*   \*

An hour went by and then another. The room was dark and silent.

I decided that the first thing I needed to do was to turn on a light. By the dim glow of the emergency light, I felt my way to the door, where I found the light switch. I flicked it on, and the room was filled with light.

That, at least, made me a drop less scared.

Another hour went by, and then I decided to try to think logically. I remembered the way my father had taught us to get out of the car. I said to myself, *I'm not two years old anymore. I have to find a way out of here.*

*　　*　　*

I looked around. Bookshelves lined the walls. Then I remembered. This was a bomb shelter. It didn't have any windows.

I also remembered that there was once a public address system in the library. I started looking, but didn't find it. There were a few locked closets, and I said to myself, *Maybe there's a PA system inside one of them, but how would I get to it? How can I open those closets?*

The closets were made out of wood. Each was locked with a big padlock. I looked around and saw a fire extinguisher. I took it and banged on the hinge of one padlock. After ten bangs, the hinge broke, and the closet door opened.

There was nothing inside but papers.

What a disappointment.

Then I said to myself, *Wait a minute. How is air getting in here? There must be a window somewhere.*

I remembered the school's new bomb shelter. It had strange windows way up high in a crawl space, and from there you could get out.

I looked around and realized that in this old bomb

shelter that had been turned into a library, they'd built closets that covered all the windows.

I started to look for a window. I climbed up on the shelves and took out books until I found a window.

It was closed. I moved the books away and opened it.

I crawled out through the window into a small space and discovered to my dismay that there was no way out. They'd built another building right next to the bomb shelter, blocking the way out.

I climbed back down, defeated, and started crying again. From frustration.

I looked at the clock. It was already ten o'clock at night. I knew that they must have started searching for me and that my parents must be frantic with worry.

What should I do?

I rested for a few more minutes, and then I started to search again for the PA system.

I had crawled under bookshelves, opened old cartons, and spent at least half an hour searching above, below, and inside closets, when I came across a box filled with old rags. I dug into it and my hand hit something hard.

It wasn't a PA system. It was a telephone. A really old one. It must have been there for years.

But I had two problems. One, it didn't have a handset, and two, it wasn't connected.

On the other hand, I reasoned, if there was a phone, there must be a wall jack somewhere, too.

I decided I'd look for the handset after I found the jack. I started looking, but I didn't find a wall jack.

I looked around again. The walls that didn't have bookshelves or closets were covered with huge posters. I said to myself, *You have no choice. You'll have to look behind the posters.*

I went from one poster to the next. I did find sockets, but not for a phone.

Behind the fourth poster I found the wall jack.

I plugged in the phone, but I had no idea if the line was still active, because there was no handset.

Suddenly I felt like I was in the story about the deaf boy who saw a boat capsizing. He dialed the police and talked and talked without having any idea if they were listening or not. But they did hear him.

At least he knew he had a working phone. I didn't even know that. The only thing I could do was try.

I knew that if I called my parents' phones, they'd see the number and maybe try to find out who it belonged to and then they'd find me.

I said a *perek* of *Tehillim* and then, with a trembling

hand, dialed my father's cell phone number. I let it ring for a while, and then I called my mother's cell phone. After that, I hung up and called our home phone. Then I dialed 100 for the police, 101 for an ambulance, and finally 102, the fire department's number.

Every two minutes I dialed those same six numbers, the only numbers I knew by heart, in that same order. I had no idea if the library's line was connected or if the telephone worked and, if it did, whether they could trace the number. I just did what I could.

An hour passed, and then I heard voices outside the door. Half a minute later, the door opened. The librarian came in followed by policemen, volunteers, and, of course, my father and mother.

*    *    *

It's hard for me to describe what went on next—the crying, the tears, and the excitement.

My parents hugged and kissed me as if they hadn't seen me in a year. I was just as emotional. One of the policemen said to me, "You're a genius. What presence of mind!"

The librarian wiped away her tears, and I thought to myself, *Once she discovers the damage I did to her library, she'll find out she has plenty of other reasons to cry.*

The policemen asked me to tell them what had happened. I led them to the place where I'd been sitting and told them the whole story. I showed them how I broke the lock, how I climbed up to the window, how I found the phone, how I found the jack, and exactly how I dialed. They said I deserved a prize in resourcefulness, and I told them that I'd already gotten it when they found me.

I went outside. A big crowd had gathered. My name had been broadcast by loudspeakers all over the neighborhood as a missing girl. Because the school is located in an isolated place, I didn't hear a thing, and even if I had heard, it wouldn't have helped me.

\*　\*　\*

The lessons that needed to be learned from my story were learned, and changes were made. They built an emergency exit to the library and installed a working phone. The librarians also got instructions to check carefully before they locked up to make sure that what happened to me wouldn't happen to anyone else.

Of all the stories I've read in my life—and there were plenty—I never dreamed that I'd be part of a breathtaking thriller. Naturally, I'd forgo the honor, but I'm not willing to forgo the lesson I learned.

Even if, G-d forbid, a kid gets trapped in a scary, tense situation, he should use his head and try to do everything he can to help himself get out of it okay. With *siyatta diShmaya*, he will succeed.

The training I got at the age of two saved my life, but in a way that had nothing to do with cars. I guess what I learned then, and in the library, is something that will stay with me my whole life.

# Glasses for the Brain

**Call me "Eli."**

That's not my real name, but it's the one I want to use to tell my story.

I'm twelve, and I'm in the sixth grade.

I'm what they call a live wire. Some might even say I'm wild. For as long as I can remember, I've gotten into fights and had problems with teachers and friends.

Even my memories as far back as pre-1A aren't all that great. Mostly I remember the corner, where I was sent on a frequent basis. In the playground, I was always getting into scrapes with the other kids. At story-telling time, I wouldn't exactly sit and listen like I was supposed to, so I got sent to the corner again and again.

To make a long story short, I got into the most trouble at times when I was supposed to pay attention and concentrate. That, plus all the stupid stuff I used to do, is what got me into trouble with friends.

When I was in the first and second grade, my situation not only didn't improve, but it got worse. I was too weak in learning and too strong during recess. I guess you could say I was also too strong in class, but not in a good way. I think that if there had been a contest to see which kid got kicked out of class the most, I would have won first prize—not only in my school, but among all the schools in town.

If it sounds like I'm bragging, I'm not. I'm really ashamed of how I was, which is why I'm writing this story under a different name.

In case you want to know why I'm even writing this story, the answer is that now I know things that I didn't know back then in first grade, and it's a shame. If I had known them then, my life would have been very, very different.

*   *   *

I've got one best friend, Motty. I have a lot of friends in class, but you can't call them real friends. They're friends to play with, to run around wild with, and also…to fight with. With some of them, I quarreled and made up and quarreled again, and with others, I didn't have such a great connection.

But Motty was different. He came to our school in

the second grade, and we became friends right away. We never fought, and we really understood each other. We tried to sit next to each other, and walk to school and back home together. The friendship was great for both of us.

I forgot to mention one thing. You're probably thinking that Motty was a troublemaker like me, and about as good in school as I was. Well, I've got a surprise for you. Motty was the smartest boy in class, believe it or not. He was also totally different than I was. He was neat and organized, calm and gentle— but don't think he was quiet. He had no problem expressing himself when he needed to and was pretty friendly, but we were very, very different in every area.

Motty was friends with everyone, something that couldn't be said about me. He never fought or got into arguments, while I…well, I already told you about me.

Our friendship was a big mystery to everyone, including my parents. But I guarded it with my life.

That's how things went until we reached the fifth grade.

\*    \*    \*

By now, my situation was impossible. I had gotten kicked out of all my afternoon classes because no teacher could teach a class I was in. I'd get out of my seat, wander around the classroom bothering kids, throwing things, acting bored… I did everything except pay attention and learn.

In the morning, the situation was better, mostly because of the teachers, who were tougher than the afternoon teachers.

One day, the principal decided that he'd had enough. He called my parents to school and informed them that until they had me evaluated, he wouldn't let me back into school.

Are you wondering what "evaluated" means? Evaluated means tested to find out why I was acting differently than all the other kids.

By this point, I was ready to admit that there was something wrong with me. Until now, I'd always defended myself by saying, "They started up with me, the classes are boring, the teacher is picking on me." This time, I was mature enough to realize that I had some kind of problem that was bothering me inside.

\*   \*   \*

We went for the evaluation. At first it was kind of fun. They gave me all sorts of tests that were more like games than tests. They showed me pictures and

asked me to tell them what they reminded me of. They said words and I had to remember them and repeat them back. They gave me sentences and asked me to explain their meaning. At the end, they had me sit in front of a computer and told me that every time I saw a dot on the screen, I should click on the mouse.

At first, I waited for the dot to appear and immediately clicked. But I got bored with the game in no time at all, because there were no people or cars. It was just a white dot that appeared suddenly someplace on the screen, and I had to wait for it.

What happened was that I started to miss. The dot would appear, and only after a second would I remember to click. After a few times like that, I got mad, and I started to click all the time, even when there was no dot. After ten minutes of that, I said, "I'm done with this stupid game."

But they told me I had to keep playing for another ten minutes. Those were the hardest ten minutes of my life. I clicked, stood up, sat down, put my feet on the table, and clicked and clicked, knowing there was no connection between my clicks and the white dots. I just didn't care.

The nightmare ended when the doctor came over and said, "Okay. You're finished."

I was happy to be released from that boring game, but he added, "You're halfway through the evaluation. In another hour, we'll give you the second half."

He handed me a glass of water and a pill and told me to swallow it. I looked at my mother, and she nodded. I swallowed the pill without hesitation.

The doctor told us to return in an hour.

*    *    *

I left with my mother. She bought me a toy and something to eat, but I was in a bad mood.

"Why are you angry?" she asked me.

"I don't know," I said. "That game got on my nerves. It was real torture to sit like that and wait for those boring little dots. Believe me, I would have gotten up and left except I didn't want to embarrass you."

My mother smiled. "Was it like you feel in class or worse?"

I thought a little, and I realized that she wasn't really asking because she needed to know the answer, but because she wanted me to understand something. She wanted me to understand why we were taking that test.

I realized that I had the same feeling during class when I felt bored and wanted to go out and play. Since

I couldn't, I'd start to move things around, pass notes, make kids laugh, throw spitballs, until eventually I'd get kicked out of class. I'd go out into the hall and feel like I'd been released from a cage…to an even more boring cage.

I told my mother some of my thoughts, and she said, "That's the reason we're here."

\* \* \*

We went back to the doctor's office. The doctor sat me in front of the computer screen again and said to me, "Now I'd like you to play that same game again."

When he said that, I wanted to run away, but I realized that this was part of the evaluation, and I knew that this evaluation was for my own good, no matter how hard it was.

I sat down in front of the computer and started to click on the mouse every time a white dot appeared, just like I had done before.

It was as boring as the first time, but this time I felt like I had the strength to keep going despite the boredom. I knew that I had a goal, and I decided to get as many points as I could. I sat there alertly in front of the screen, and the minute a dot appeared, I clicked. Ten minutes passed that way, then twenty. When the doctor came to tell me that the test was over, I could hardly believe it had gone by so quickly.

We waited a few minutes, and then the evaluator called us into a room and sat with me and my mother.

He told us that according to the tests he had done, I had a very hard time with what he called "attention and concentration." He described to me what happens when I have to pay attention to a teacher or concentrate on something. It feels like real torture to me, and then I look for things that will distract me from the torture.

He also said that every little thing disturbs my concentration, which makes it hard for me to pay attention and understand the material, despite other tests that showed that when something interested me, I could understand a lot more than most kids my age.

This really confused me. My mother, too.

"Do you mean to tell me that my son could learn Gemara better than most of his boys in his class?" my mother asked in amazement.

"I don't know his classmates, but your son has above-average intelligence. That means that if we divide all the children in the world into ten groups, from weak to genius, your son is one step under genius.

"However," the doctor continued, "his problem

with attention and concentration prevents him from focusing and learning as he could. It's like a pot that's tightly covered. No matter how much you try to pour water into it, nothing can get in."

"So what do we do?" my mother asked.

"That's why we did that last test, which is called the T.O.V.A. test. We gave you a boring test, like a boring class, and you failed it miserably. In the beginning, you did fine, but as soon as you became less interested in the game, you started to miss, and when you became thoroughly bored, you clicked at random."

He showed me the results, and I was really embarrassed. They were way too low.

"Then I gave you that small pill. Remember?" the doctor said to me with a smile.

"Yes," I replied.

"After an hour, when the pill took effect, you took the same test again. Now look at the results."

I looked at the computer printout the doctor showed me. It was hard to believe that the same kid who had gotten such a bad score the first time got such an excellent score only an hour later on the same test.

"I'll give you a prescription for the pills," the doctor said. "You'll take one every morning, and what happened to you here with the computer game will happen to you in school as well. You'll also find it easier to get along with your friends."

"What's the name of the pill?" I asked.

"Ritalin," the doctor said—and the minute he said that, I knew I'd never agree to take it.

* * *

We left the doctor's office.

"Let's go to the pharmacy to buy the pills," my mother said.

"Ima," I said, "it's a waste of time. I'm not going to take that Ritalin!"

"Why not?"

"In fact, I'm really angry that he even gave such a thing to me!"

"What are you talking about?" my mother asked in astonishment.

"You don't know how many kids have said to me over the years, 'You need Ritalin.' At first, I didn't know what they were talking about. I finally asked and they told me it's a pill for kids with problems. What am I, a kid with problems?"

My mother didn't answer.

"Okay! So I'm a kid with problems," I threw out,

insulted. "And one of my problems is that I'm not going to take those pills!"

My mother went and bought the pills anyway.

I was burning mad the whole way home.

The next morning, I refused to take the pill. My parents pleaded with me to try it just once, but I dug in my heels. No way was I going to take those pills, and I told them so.

"You're not going to make me into a problem kid!" I shouted.

I went to school, my problems continued and even got worse, but I refused to hear another word about those pills.

*    *    *

In the meantime, I suffered one humiliation after the other. I was behind the class in all subjects, and my run-ins with teachers and friends didn't stop. There wasn't a week that went by when I didn't hear someone say, "You need Ritalin." I'd feel hurt and react angrily, which got me into even more trouble. My parents saw how much I was suffering and repeatedly tried to convince me to try it, but nothing they said got me to change my mind.

I graduated fifth grade and went into sixth, not

caring one way or the other. In the very first month, I was kicked out of class by the teacher, who didn't allow any disturbances in his class and who was very sarcastic toward me. He said the class was at a certain level, and anyone who wasn't up to that level could not remain in the class.

That put a lot of pressure on me, and I also felt very hurt. I saw my friends learning, paying attention in class, making progress, and growing more serious, while I was still busy with foolishness, not paying attention, and getting into trouble all the time.

The one bright spot in my life was my friend Motty, who ignored my situation and stayed unbelievably loyal.

*　*　*

One day, when we were walking home together after a day full of mishaps, Motty said to me, "Tell me something, Eli. Did you ever think about maybe taking Ritalin?"

I looked at him in shock. "What? What did you say?"

"Ritalin," he repeated. "Haven't you ever heard of it?"

"Tell me something, aren't you ashamed to hurt my feelings like that?"

"I didn't mean to hurt your feelings. I just—"

"I don't want to know you," I said and ran home.

The next day, I didn't talk to Motty at all. We sat next to each other, but I ignored him. In the beginning, he looked at me and tried to catch my eye, but he caught on fast that I was mad at him, and he gave up trying.

One day passed, then another. A week went by like that. It was the first time since I'd known Motty that we'd had a fight. By then, I realized that he hadn't meant to hurt my feelings, but I didn't know how to make things right again.

After school, Motty was waiting for me outside.

"Listen to me, Eli," he said. "I want you to come to my house. I want to talk to you. If we don't make up, we'll be mad at each other forever, and we'll even have to move our seats. Just give me a chance."

Actually, I wanted to make up with him, too. He was giving me a way out.

I went with him to his house, still not saying a word.

\*    \*    \*

We sat in his room. There were a few minutes of embarrassed silence, and then Motty said to me, "I want to tell you a few things, but promise me right now that you won't run away like the last time, even if I tell you the most painful things in the world. Agreed?"

I gave it some thought, and then said, "Agreed."

"Why were you so angry at me?" he asked.

"You know why."

"Why were you so angry at me?" he asked again.

"Because you told me to take…that pill."

"It's called Ritalin," Motty said. Then he asked me, "So what made you mad at me?"

"Why are you playing innocent? You hurt my feelings. As if I need Ritalin!"

"Eli, you know yourself better than I do. Do you think you need Ritalin?"

"Will you stop it already!"

"No. You promised that you would answer me and not run away. Do you need it or not?"

"*No!*" I said, furious.

"No?"

"I don't know…"

"I think you do know, Eli. If you don't know, I'll tell you. You have a problem with attention and concentration and you're a little hyper. It's a fact. It doesn't make you a problem kid. Not at all. You're my best friend, and I think you're nice, pleasant, and interesting. But you have a problem with attention and concentration. Period."

We didn't say anything for a while, and then I said, "I'm ashamed of it."

"Ashamed of what?"

"That Ritalin."

"Tell me something," he said, "why aren't you ashamed of your glasses?"

"Why should I be?" I asked in surprise.

"Because they tell the world that you have a problem with your eyesight. The minute you wear glasses, everyone knows."

"So what if I have a problem with my eyesight? Am I supposed to be ashamed of that?"

"What about if you have a problem with paying attention and concentrating? Are you supposed to be ashamed of that?"

That was a good answer if ever there was one. I didn't have an answer to it.

"Take off your glasses," he said.

I raised my eyebrows, but I did what he said.

"Try to read the titles of my books over there on the bookshelf."

I tried, but I couldn't. My prescription is minus three. I couldn't read the titles without my glasses.

"Look around you. Everything is blurry. You can't even see my lip movements clearly. Everything is out of focus. Correct?"

"Correct."

"That's how the brain of someone who has a problem with attention and concentration feels when it isn't wearing the 'glasses of the brain,'" Motty said. "Now put your glasses back on."

I did what he said. Naturally, everything became clear. In one second, I saw all the book titles and Motty's lips moving as he talked.

"That's how the brain feels when someone takes a tiny pill called Ritalin," Motty said. "And if you think taking Ritalin is something to be ashamed of, well, there's more to be ashamed of by acting like someone who needs Ritalin and *doesn't* take it. It's exactly like someone who needs glasses and has a really high number deciding that he doesn't want people to know he has a vision problem. He walks around bumping into people and running into poles, and then everyone can really see what a big problem he has."

Motty didn't stop there. "You know what the difference is between glasses and Ritalin? With Ritalin, no one knows you're taking it. What they see is your good behavior. But when you don't take it, everyone sees the problem and also tells you all the time, 'You need Ritalin.' So what did you gain?"

I remained silent. What he had said made a lot of sense, and it didn't hurt my feelings at all. I didn't know what to say, but suddenly a suspicion arose in my mind.

"Tell me something, did my parents talk to you? How did you suddenly become this big expert in attention and concentration and pills?" I asked, half suspicious and half mocking.

Motty didn't look surprised. It looked like he had anticipated that question.

"I asked you to come here because I wanted to give you a present."

"What's the connection?" I said. "I asked a question and—"

He handed me a brown envelope and said, "Open it. And if you still have any questions, shoot."

I opened it. Inside was a blue-and-white box of medicine just like the one my mother had bought. It was Ritalin.

I didn't understand how he had it. What was going on?

That's when he dropped the bomb.

"I've been taking Ritalin since the second grade. If

you'll recall, I went to a different school for pre-1A and first grade. I was the most disruptive kid in my school, to the point where they refused to let me continue there. Over summer vacation between first grade and second, my parents took me for an evaluation. They found out that I had a serious problem with attention and concentration. They gave me Ritalin, and, unlike you, maybe because I was younger, I took it without putting up a fight."

I closed my eyes. "I'm in shock! You're the top boy in the class. Do you mean to tell me that all these years…"

"I took the glasses for the brain, and they removed the problem that prevented me from paying attention, from learning, and from being a calm kid. Now you know everything."

In that split second, I knew a lot but not everything. How stupid I'd been! How smart Motty was! What an idiot I'd been to deny the problem instead of solving it. I'd have never guessed that Motty had a problem with attention and concentration, and that was only because he was taking medication, not because he refused to take it.

Thoughts flashed through my mind one after the other, and then I came to the biggest realization of all.

What a great friend I had! What a present he gave me! It wasn't a present you could buy in any store. It was a present that people hardly ever give. Motty had given me a secret—his secret. He did it only for me. I would never have known if he hadn't told me, and he told me only so that I'd be able to solve my own problem.

\* \* \*

I thanked Motty with all my heart. Then I went home and told my mother that I wanted her to go to the pharmacy and buy Ritalin.

My mother didn't know what had happened to me after I'd been so stubborn about it for a whole year.

From the day I started taking that medication, I changed dramatically. I started to pay attention, to understand, to concentrate, to shine. Within a few months, the boys in class were arguing over who was a better student, me or Motty. Naturally, both of us were willing to let the other one be the best, but I was suddenly discovering the talents I had, which had been hidden in a pot whose cover is tightly closed.

My behavior changed dramatically, too, and my teachers and principal didn't stop praising me for the amazing change that had taken place in me. It reached the point where everyone forgot I'd ever been any different.

Now I'm in the sixth grade. I'm smart and successful, and I believe that my future is bright.

But no matter what will be, I'll always remember my faithful friend Motty and the real friendship he showed me. And I'll never forget the wonderful present he gave me.

Glasses for the brain.

# Entrance Exam

**My name is Yechezkel.**

I'm twelve, and I live in Haifa.

I'm a fairly quiet kid, but popular. If you see a bunch of noisy kids and one kid in the middle who's calm but totally part of the group—it might be me.

Ever since I can remember, I've been popular. Grades are another matter. Mine have never been especially good. It's not that I'm stupid or anything like that. It's just that I never liked to learn or pay attention. I preferred to fiddle with all sorts of things during class, or, if I had a teacher who didn't let students do that sort of stuff, I'd just daydream.

The advantage of daydreaming is that no one knows you're not paying attention. Your eyes are focused on the teacher, but your mind is elsewhere—anyplace but the lesson, the classroom, or the Gemara.

Actually, it's not accurate to say that no one knows.

The teachers always knew that I was daydreaming. True, it took them a little time (but not much) until they found me out. "At first I thought you paid more attention than any other boy in class, because I rarely see a student whose eyes are always on the teacher," one told me. "But as time went on, I realized that something was wrong. Your eyes had a glazed look. You were looking at me, but your mind was far, far away."

There was also proof of my "superior attention" in the form of my test marks. They were so low that I'm ashamed to tell you what they were.

I was considered a lazy student, and I didn't like it one bit.

\*   \*   \*

The difference between me and the other lazy kids in class was that when they were bored, they started acting up in class. And when you act up, you get into trouble.

Getting into trouble means being sent out of class, having to bring a note home to your parents, getting sent to the principal, being suspended—all the things that happen to kids who act up in class. I never went through those experiences, because I never made any trouble. Even though the teachers eventually caught on that I wasn't paying attention, either because of my test results or because of my glazed look, they didn't punish me. After all, there's no law that says how a student's eyes have to look during class. As long as I didn't disrupt, they pretty much left me alone.

You might think that was a good thing. But actually it wasn't. While the kids who made trouble were forced to control themselves and pay attention to avoid punishment, I didn't get any punishments, so I stayed lazy.

\*　\*　\*

When I entered the seventh grade, my life changed.

The seventh-grade teacher, Rabbi Shaltiel, was the type of teacher who wasn't satisfied with good behavior alone. He had very high expectations of his students and was unwilling to compromise.

What was interesting was that Rabbi Shaltiel paid no attention to disturbances. If he did react, it was not with a fiery speech and punishments. No, with him it was short and to the point. A look. A word. Nothing more.

The gang of "backbenchers" (which is what he called the boys who grabbed the last seats at the beginning of the year in order to be as far away from the teacher as possible) quickly caught on that something fundamental had changed. Somehow this teacher had managed to create an atmosphere in which they felt ashamed to disturb, just like a boy in the eighth grade would be ashamed to play in a sandbox.

Having no choice, they started to learn seriously. Some of the biggest troublemakers turned into the best students, something that surprised us all. Soon everyone was swept up in a spirit of healthy competition that propelled the whole class higher and higher.

Who do you think was left all alone at the bottom? Me, of course.

\*   \*   \*

At first, it didn't bother me, but it soon did, because Rabbi Shaltiel didn't let me do what every other teacher had—daydream. He'd ask me to read, and then fifteen minutes later he'd say, "*Nu*, Chesky, what do you say about that?" (I had no idea what "that" was...) He would make me participate and not let me drift off into my own thoughts.

I wasn't asking for much. All I wanted to do was dream.

And I managed to keep doing just that, in my own way. Though I had plenty of uncomfortable moments, that still wasn't enough to get me to change—both because I was used to my status as lazy, and also because I didn't know how to get out of it.

But Rabbi Shaltiel wasn't about to give up.

\*    \*    \*

One day, Rabbi Shaltiel announced that from now on a mark of 80 percent on Gemara tests would be the threshold. He also explained what that meant. He said it was like the threshold of a doorway. Anyone who didn't get over 80 wasn't worthy of crossing the threshold of the classroom and wouldn't be until he took a repeat exam and brought his grade up to 80.

For me, this was bad news. My grades were usually lower than 60, and I don't want to get into how much lower they were than that. A grade of 80 seemed beyond my reach.

It was the first time I found myself trying to pay attention in order to somehow follow the material being learned. I wouldn't say I succeeded all that well.

On the first test after the announcement, I got one of the highest test marks in my life: 65. Still, it was fifteen points away from the threshold grade.

When the teacher passed out the graded tests, he announced that some of us hadn't passed the threshold.

Those boys wouldn't be able to enter the classroom until they did.

He didn't say the boys' names, but it was only a matter of time until everyone knew. Tomorrow, whoever didn't come into the classroom hadn't passed.

\*     \*     \*

The next day, I woke up both nervous and curious. I was nervous because I didn't know how I'd bridge the gap and pass the test. And I was curious to see who else had failed along with me.

I davened with a minyan, arrived in school on time, and waited for the bell to ring signaling the start of school. In a minute, everyone was swallowed up inside the classrooms.

Everyone except two.

Me and Yoni.

I was surprised and yet not surprised. Yoni was a former backbencher, so it wasn't strange for him to be outside the classroom. On the other hand, since we'd started learning in Rabbi Shaltiel's class, he'd made unbelievable progress and turned into one of the most outstanding boys in the class.

"What happened?" I asked him.

He shrugged.

I assumed he was too embarrassed to answer me, and I regretted asking him. It dawned on me that he probably pretended to pay attention just like I did, but didn't learn a thing—which made him a better actor than I was. He not only pretended to pay attention, but from time to time asked a question, as if he was really following, and the teacher would praise him for it. Well, I guess test marks never lie…

"What now?" I asked him.

"We learn, that's what," he answered.

Yoni went to the principal's office and got a copy of the test we hadn't passed from the secretary.

"I suggest we go over the questions," he said, "and what we don't know, we can learn together."

That's what we did. Yoni went back to class to get our Gemaras (I didn't dare go in there, because I was too embarrassed), we found an empty classroom, and we started going over the questions.

It was a lot easier than I'd thought. The questions were straightforward, and all we needed to do was to find the place in the Gemara or *Rashi* where we'd find the answer and learn it.

After that, we wrote down the answers on the test paper, and during the break, we handed in the papers to the teacher.

Rabbi Shaltiel went into the teachers' room to grade our tests. We waited with nervous anticipation. Ten minutes later, he came out and said, "You both passed. You can return to the classroom."

That bought me peace and quiet for a week.

During that week, I tried to pay attention, but without too much success. When it came time for the test, I failed again. Along with Yoni.

Once again, we had to remain outside the classroom. We sat and learned for the repeat test, took it, handed it in, and…we passed.

When Rabbi Shaltiel gave us back our tests, he surprised us by saying, "Until now, you've had it easy, because you've taken the makeup test with open Gemaras. Starting from the next time, the test will be with closed Gemaras. I'll sit with you and make sure you don't copy from each other."

That was bad news, because I relied on Yoni a lot, both for the learning and when it came time to take the test.

You might say he even dictated it to me…

\*   \*   \*

I had no choice but to put a lot more effort into paying attention. Still, I didn't pass this time either. My mark on the test was pretty high for me—76—but I didn't pass the threshold.

The same for Yoni.

We learned together, with me trying to concentrate and remember as much as possible. Then we went into the teachers' room to take the repeat test, without open Gemaras and without any help.

I started to take the test, and believe it or not, I saw that I knew enough to pass the threshold. I finished writing, gave the test to the rebbe, and waited.

He returned the tests to us a few minutes later and said, "You both passed. But next week the conditions are going to be tougher. The repeat test will have different questions written especially for that test. You will not be able to count on the first test."

That's what he said, and then he left.

\* \* \*

I sat there with Yoni feeling pretty bitter. "Why is he doing this to us?" I complained.

"I think he caught on that we're building on the original test and only reviewing the questions we missed."

"So what? What if we are? I think he's got it in for us, that's what."

Yoni shrugged. "Maybe. Let's make sure he's got nothing to find."

The next test was on especially hard material, so it was pushed off until after Shavuos.

"Perfect!" Yoni declared. "Let's try to pass the threshold the first time around, instead of going through the humiliation of having to take a repeat again."

"How exactly do you think we can do that?" I asked him.

"Shavuos night," he suggested, "we'll be *chavrusas*, and we'll review the material all night."

I agreed.

It was the first time in my life that I really learned all night on Shavuos. That night had always been a night of fun and games for me. I'd play outside with my friends, go inside for coffee or cocoa, go back outside again, then come to davening and fall asleep. That's pretty much the picture of how I spent Shavuos.

This time it was different. Yoni and I made up to meet an hour after the meal, and we just sat there and learned continuously. We reviewed all the material that had been covered, and though it was hard, we were able to understand it and even feel like we had mastered it.

Toward morning, an elbow landed on each of

our shoulders. We turned around. It was Rav Shaltiel taking a "tour" of the *batei medrash* to check up on his students.

"Well, look who I see here!" he said with a big smile. In his hands were two cups of tea that he'd prepared for us.

Now I knew why he'd put an elbow on my shoulder and not a hand.

*　*　*

The test took place the day after Shavuos. The next day, we anxiously awaited the return of our test papers.

"This time, everyone passed the threshold!" the teacher announced.

He started handing back the tests. I waited tensely to see my grade.

It was perfect—100. For the first time in my life.

I filed the test in the folder that Rav Shaltiel had given us at the beginning of the year and ran over to Yoni.

We were alone in the classroom. All the other boys had gone out for recess, and Yoni was busy putting his test in his folder, too.

"You won't believe it!" I said to him excitedly. "I got a hundred! What did you get? Show me!"

He showed me his test. He got a hundred, too.

"That's really great for us," I said. "It's the first time I've ever gotten a hundred. Take a look at my folder and see how far I've come."

I showed him all my tests since the beginning of the year: 40, 45, 42, 50, 45, 65. Pretty bad. Suddenly there was a 75 that got changed to an 85, and after that a 70 that was changed to an 80. The marks kept going up and up until a repeat test got 90, then 95, until finally, the last test (and the real test)—without any second test.

One hundred.

"Look how far I've come," I told him happily. "Now show me your folder."

Yoni tried to get out of it.

"What do you care?" I told him. "You got better marks than I did anyway. What do you have to be ashamed of?"

I saw that he was really feeling pressured, but I ignored it. I took his folder and started to flip through it.

What I saw there left me totally surprised.

All his marks, from beginning to end, were 100. Even the original tests, not just the repeats.

"What's going on?" I wondered aloud. "I don't get it. What's this supposed to mean? You got one 100 after another. Why did you have to take the repeat tests?"

Yoni didn't answer. He looked really uncomfortable.

All of a sudden, we noticed that we weren't alone in the classroom. Our teacher, Rabbi Shaltiel, had been watching us the whole time, and now he came over to us.

"I'll explain it to you, Chesky," he said.

"As you noticed, most of the boys in class made a lot of progress. Yoni, who was one of the backbenchers, made the biggest change. He really took off. While you, though you weren't considered a problem boy or one who disturbed the class, remained right where you were.

"It was my idea to ask Yoni to land next to you so that you could take off together. He agreed to accept the humiliation of being 'one of the boys who didn't pass the threshold.' He said that he was already immune to humiliation because in past years he'd been outside the classroom more than in.

"And it worked. Together you've soared to greater and greater heights, and now you've gotten the highest grade. But it wasn't so much the grade that interested me as the *geshmak*. *Geshmak* in learning is the only thing a *ben Torah* needs. When I saw you together on Shavuos night, I saw real light and joy on your faces. I saw that your eyes were focused, not glazed over or dreaming. You looked really alert. Finally, you were alive, just like it says, '*Vechai bahem*—And live by them.' That's far more important to me than your test marks.

"You passed the threshold," Rabbi Shaltiel added. "Not only the grade threshold, but the threshold for receiving the honorable title of *ben Torah*."

*   *   *

Almost a year has passed since then. I'm graduating the eighth grade and about to enter a top yeshivah.

Last week, the date arrived that I feel changed my life. Shavuos night. Naturally, I made up with my regular *chavrusa* to learn through the night.

It was Yoni, of course. He's a true friend, because it's thanks to him that I took off and got to where I am now.

# And the Winner Is...?

**My name is Chaya.**

I'm eleven years old, in the fifth grade, and I live in Jerusalem.

I'm full of energy and very outgoing. I'm not the type to sit inside the classroom during recess. Not me. I enjoy every second of recess from beginning to end.

I'm the one who chooses the games we play, like tag, hide-and-seek, and blind man's bluff, or games with a ball, like dodgeball.

Ever since I've been in kindergarten, those games have led to fights. For instance, whenever we played tag, the girls who were caught denied it, while the girls who had caught them claimed that they were "it."

We even fought over jump rope. Girls who were told that they were out would argue that "the rope wasn't turned the right way." Other girls said the rules were different than what they really were. As you can imagine, these fights ruined the games and caused a lot of angry feelings.

A year ago, my class had a big blow-up during a game of blind man's bluff. The girl who was "it" cheated. I saw her peeking out from under her blindfold. That's the only reason she caught me. How did I know? Because she chased after me just like in tag, as if her eyes weren't blindfolded. Everyone knows what that means.

I went home angry and told my mother about it. She smiled.

I asked her why she was smiling, why she wasn't saying anything, but she seemed reluctant to tell me. I pleaded with her to explain, and finally she said, "Did you ever check to see how many of these fights start with you?"

"I'm not the one who starts the fights," I protested. "They are."

"If that's what you're saying, then everything's okay," my mother said, but her tone of voice told me that she was thinking the exact opposite.

*   *   *

A few months passed. One day I came home hurt

and angry. I had fought with practically the whole class because of a girl who lied and said I had dropped the ball in a game of dodgeball. If it was true, that meant I was out of the game. But it wasn't true. I caught the ball and then I fell down, but the ball was still in my hand. Everyone said that the ball fell out of my hand and that I lay on top of it so that they'd think it hadn't dropped. An argument broke out that broke up the game. My friends blamed me and said it was impossible to play with me.

I was really upset and hurt. I walked home angry and crying hard. I had a good reason to cry, too. When I fell, I'd gotten a big bruise on my hand, leg, and face. My cheek was even bleeding.

I felt bitter and betrayed. Not only had I gotten hurt, but every single girl there had said I was out. I didn't know which hurt more.

When I got home, my mother took care of me right away. She washed my cuts, gently dabbed on disinfectant, covered my cheek with a big bandage, and wrapped up my arm in an elastic bandage.

Then she sat down to talk with me. She wanted to know what had happened.

I told her.

My mother didn't say anything.

"Don't you think my friends are horrible?" I asked her.

My mother remained silent for a moment, and then she said to me, "You know what I think about the subject."

"No, I don't know."

"Maybe because you want to run away from the truth," my mother said. "We talked about this the last time you fought with your friends."

"So tell me again."

"I think that in large part these fights are your fault."

That was hard for me to hear. I thought my mother would be on my side. What I really wanted was for her to say that the other girls were to blame.

"Look, Chaya, I've been watching you play with other kids since you were in nursery school, here at home and in the playground, and I've noticed something very interesting about you. You *must* win."

I thought about what she was saying, and then I said, "Yes, I do like to win. Is that a problem?"

"It is," my mother said, "but it's a small problem. The bigger problem is that you don't know how to lose."

"What's the difference?"

"There's a huge difference between the two," my mother said. "Almost every girl wants to win. But a girl who *has* to win isn't really playing. She's fighting a battle. And that's the problem. Because a girl who can't lose makes everyone else who's playing with her suffer. She doesn't let anyone else win, and when she loses, she starts arguments that make everyone fed up with playing with her."

I didn't tell my mother, but that's exactly what they had said to me: "We're fed up with playing with you."

"But no one likes to lose," I said.

"True," my mother said, "but most girls play games for fun. When they play, they enjoy every minute of it. If they win, they're even happier, but their enjoyment doesn't vanish if they lose. With you, it's all about winning. You don't enjoy the game, but the victory. If you lose, you're so disappointed that it turns the game into a nightmare for you, and when you argue and fight for fairness as you see it, it ruins it for the others. I'm surprised they even agree to play with you."

I didn't say anything. Secretly, I was happy that my mother didn't know how close I was to just that, having all my friends refuse to play with me.

"So what should I do?" I asked.

"I think we should go to Bubby," my mother said.

"Bubby? Why?"

"I was just like you when I was your age. I felt that I had to win, and I wasn't willing to lose. One day, your grandmother told me a story that changed my life *and* the way I acted. I think that the time has come for you to hear the story, too."

\* \* \*

The very next day, after school, my mother took me to my grandmother's house.

My grandmother lives in a nursing home not too far from us, and we visit her every Shabbos and sometimes during the week as well.

We went into her room, and my mother said, "Chaya's here." I realized that she'd already spoken to Bubby about the subject.

Bubby asked, "Would you like to go outside so that Mrs. Holtz won't hear our conversation?"

Mrs. Holtz was Bubby's roommate. They knew each other before my grandmother moved to the nursing home, and at a certain point my grandmother suggested that she move in with her, since both of them were widows.

I thought about it and decided that it was better if we stayed in the room and didn't go out to the lobby where everyone could hear us. Besides, my grand-mother's roommate spoke mostly Yiddish, so I didn't think she'd understand all that much.

My grandmother started to tell me her story.

"It happened more than sixty-five years ago," my grandmother said. "I was eight years old, and an only child. We lived in Poland in a big mansion. We were very wealthy, with servants to clean the house and serve the meals. I had everything a girl could wish for…"

\* \* \*

One day (my grandmother continued), the Nazis invaded Poland. Within a short time, they had taken away my father's factory and confiscated everything we had. We were forced to wear a yellow star on our clothes, and every day brought new restrictions and terrible decrees. My father looked worried all the time. He said he sensed that the Nazis had decided to kill all the Jews.

We didn't believe it. My mother argued with him and said he was exaggerating. But my father insisted he was right.

"If they try to take us away, we must refuse," he said. "We'll have to flee or go into hiding. No matter what happens, we can't let them take us, because the Germans have no use for Jews except to kill them."

A week later, a few SS men came and took my father away. They surprised us while we were in the middle of eating supper, and my father didn't have time to escape. He said good-bye to me, whispered something in my mother's ear, and left. I never saw him again.

We cried for a whole week. At the end of that week, the Germans ordered all the Jews to gather in the main square. From there they would be transported to a work camp. My father's parting words were still fresh in my mother's mind, and she told me what he had whispered to her.

"When he left, your father said that we should go to Anna's house and pay her to hide us."

Anna was our servant. She had been with my parents from their wedding day, and they had always treated her very well. My father assumed that for the right price, she would agree to take us in.

My mother packed a suitcase with our clothes and retrieved thousands of rubles from their hiding place to take with us. As all the other Jews in town streamed to the central square, we ran to Anna's house.

Anna lived in a working-class neighborhood on the top floor of a five-story building. We knocked on the door, and Anna opened it. She was shocked to see us standing there. My mother begged her to hide us. Her pleas, and the huge payment she promised for each month that Anna hid us, convinced our former servant to let us stay.

Anna gave us a tiny room with one bed that my mother and I shared. Over the next few weeks, the situation grew increasingly tense. The Germans declared that any Polish citizen caught hiding a Jew would be killed. We were worried. We knew that at any moment Anna might turn us in. My mother decided to discuss it with her.

Anna cried and said that she didn't mind hiding us, but she was also afraid of the Germans coming and killing her.

My mother said that if the Germans made a search of the building, we'd jump down to the second-floor balcony and escape from there. The Germans would never know where we had hidden, because none of the neighbors even suspected that we were hiding in Anna's apartment. The idea of jumping down from the fifth floor all the way to the second story scared us, but the idea of Anna turning us in was even more scary.

Anna asked for time to think it over. In the end, she informed my mother that she agreed to the arrangement, as long as my mother promised that the minute the Germans stepped onto the third floor, both of us would jump from her fifth-floor balcony to the balcony on the second floor without any arguments. My mother shook Anna's hand on the promise, and in return, we gained peace.

For a while.

\* \* \*

During this time, we remained hidden in our room, quiet as could be. Every so often, I was allowed to play with Anna's daughter, Julia, who was my age. We played all kinds of quiet games, mostly chess and cat's cradle.

I was very good at chess. I'd played all the girls in my class and won every single game. Then the girls in the higher grades challenged me, and I beat them, too. Naturally, Julia was no match for me, and I won our games easily every time.

We'd been playing for about a week when I smugly told my mother how I beat my friend all the time. My mother sat down on the bed and said to me, "Shifra, what you're doing isn't good. I want you to let her win."

"Let her win? Why?"

"You've got to understand that every day we are living here is a miracle. Hashem put it into the minds of these gentiles to view us in a positive light. We need to make every effort to make sure they keep that attitude. I want you to know that jealousy is a very dangerous thing. Who knows if the gentiles' jealousy of us is not what caused all these troubles to come upon us here in Poland in the first place? You have to restrain your natural desire to win and instead let her feel the satisfaction of beating you."

"But Mama, she's my best friend. I don't think she's jealous of me."

"Sometimes you can't see jealousy. Besides, it's not enough that she's not jealous. You have to make her love you. I am ordering you to do this, Shifra. From now on, make sure you lose. And do it in such a way that she thinks she won on her own and not because you let her win."

I found it very hard. It was one thing to let my friend win if she knew I was letting her win. That way, I could have kept my self-respect. But for her to think that she was beating me fair and square? I found that almost impossible. Still, that very same day, I lost a game of chess for the first time in my life.

I couldn't believe how happy Julia was about her

win. She ran to tell her mother, who treated us especially well that day. Not once did she have that irritated look on her face that said, "I have no choice, but how I wish you'd leave!"

The next day, I let Julia win a few times, and then I beat her twice so she wouldn't get suspicious. The following day, I beat her once, and from then on, I let her win almost every game. Every so often, when my mother told me to, I'd win a game so that my playmate's satisfaction in beating me wouldn't diminish.

It was the same with the other games we played. I let her make up the rules and win to the extent that I forgot all about the possibility of my winning and her losing. She did, too.

One day, we heard the sound of trucks. The Nazis had come to search our street.

Anna woke us up. Her face was as white as chalk. "The Germans are here! Do you remember our agreement?"

My mother also turned pale. "I remember."

"Then let's go," she said in a voice that brooked no argument. "Get dressed."

I was too scared to cry. My mother looked at Anna and clearly saw what I was seeing: steely determination. My mother didn't even try to argue. She packed our things quickly. As if that would help us after we jumped down to the second-floor balcony! Who knew if we'd even survive the jump? Even if we did, the Germans would probably catch us.

We went to the living room, to the window from which we were supposed to jump down to the second-floor balcony. I can still picture it, as if I'm watching the scene unfold in slow motion—how we walked into the living room, my mother holding the suitcase and me clutching my doll, only eight years old but wise enough to realize that we were heading into grave danger. I didn't know which was worse, jumping down to the second floor, and our possible deaths, or being captured by the Germans.

I followed my mother. I didn't cry. Fear must have frozen even my tears. We walked over to the window, and that's where we encountered an obstacle.

Anna's daughter Julia, the one who had beaten me at all those games for the past two years, stood in our way. "I don't want them to jump," she declared.

Her mother didn't even answer her. She just went over to Julia and took her arm to pull her away.

Julia stood firm and started to shout in protest. Her mother put a hand over her mouth. "You'll give us away to the Germans!" she hissed.

"I don't care! I don't want them to jump."

Anna kept her hand over Julia's mouth as she tried to drag her away, but Julia went wild. She wriggled out of her mother's grip, grabbed the window frame, and screamed. Even I knew that she was putting herself in danger.

Her mother relented. "What do you want us to do?" she asked.

"Let them go up to the roof," Julia said. "There's a wooden shed that Shifra and I built. They can hide there."

Anna's eyes were shooting daggers, but we could hear the Germans in the stairwell, and she knew she had no choice.

"Very well. Follow me."

She went over to the front door, opened it cautiously, and peered into the stairwell. The Germans were on the third floor by now. She snuck us over to the makeshift ladder that led to the roof. We quickly climbed up. Then my mother pulled up the ladder and closed the door behind us as quietly as she could—just as the Germans exited a third-floor apartment and entered the stairwell.

We hid in the shack Julia and I had made. I said *tehillim*, begging Hashem to save us. We remained there

for a few hours without knowing what was going on outside. We didn't dare move, let alone leave our miserable shed to find out.

Suddenly we heard a girl singing. Well, it wasn't exactly a song but more like the victory chant Julia sang whenever she won a game: "I beat *Shif*-ra, I beat *Shif*-ra..."

We left the shed, pulled open the door, lowered the ladder, and climbed down to the apartment. As soon as we walked in, Julia hugged me hard and started chanting again, to the same tune, "We beat *Hit*-ler, we beat *Hit*-ler."

Back in our room, I hugged my mother. I didn't need to say anything. It was obvious to me that her wise advice had saved our lives.

\*   \*   \*

"The Germans never came back," my grandmother said. "The war ended, and we made aliyah. My mother remarried and began a new family. I grew up, got married, and raised a beautiful family of my own. Poland was taken over by the communists. It was terrible for the people there. They were like inmates in one big prison, sentenced to a life of poverty and suffering. Anyone who dared complain was taken away and shot.

"That was the punishment given to the country that had helped the Nazis spill the blood of three million Jews out of the total six million Jews that were killed in the Holocaust. We were blessed to come to the Holy Land, where we lived a pleasant, good life, and merited to see children and wonderful grandchildren. Like you, Chaya.

"So that's my story," my grandmother said, "and I think that it should be told to every single boy or girl, or even teen and grown-up, who is determined to win—or, worse, who doesn't know how to lose—no matter what the price. It turns out that other people don't like to lose either, certainly not every time.

"Let the other person win. And nothing will happen if you tell him about your failures. He won't take pleasure in them, but instead will be encouraged to know that he's not the only one who fails sometimes."

I didn't say anything. The story was a little bit scary, but very interesting. I could hardly believe it had happened to my very own grandmother.

"How did you like the story, Chaya?" my grandmother asked me.

I didn't know what to say.

"You look sad," my grandmother said. "Why? The story had a happy ending, didn't it?"

"I'm thinking about myself," I said. "I wonder what I would have done if I had been in your place. It's a scary thought.

"I know that you had a reason for telling me this story. You want me to learn from what you did, and I realize now that I don't want to be the person who has to win at any cost."

"Good," my grandmother said. "Then it was worthwhile telling it to you."

"But something is bothering me."

"What is it, darling?"

"Julia," I said. "I'm thinking about her. She was left back there in Poland. I'm wondering what happened to her under the communists. She didn't really deserve…"

My grandmother smiled. "What a good heart you have, Chaya. Don't worry. I'll tell you what happened to Julia. For more than forty years, we didn't hear a thing from Anna or Julia. With the fall of the Iron Curtain, they contacted us, and we were able to express our gratitude by having them honored with the title 'Righteous Gentile.'"

"Are they still alive?" I wanted to know.

"Anna is no longer living. She died many years ago. But her daughter Julia is alive and well. She came to Israel and converted to Judaism. In fact, you know her, though you never knew her story."

My jaw dropped.

"Yes, Chaya, let me introduce you to my childhood friend Julia. You know her as my roommate, Leah Holtz."

# Double Prize

**My name is Rafael.**

I'm eleven, and I live in Beitar Illit.

I'm considered a good student and a friendly kid. You could say I'm not quiet and not loud, but somewhere in the middle.

Once a week I participate in Masmidim, an after-school learning program for boys my age. We review material that we learn in yeshivah, and sometimes the *ben Torah* who learns with us tells us a story.

My parents didn't ask me to join the Masmidim program. My father said that my long hours of learning in school are enough, but since I asked if I could join, my parents had no problem agreeing to my going.

From time to time, they give out prizes in Masmidim. When that happens, everyone piles up on the group leader, as if there won't be enough prizes to go around. If you'd ask every boy why he was jumping and begging for a prize that he was going to get anyway, not a single one would be able to give you an answer. That's just how kids are when prizes are given out. Every kid pushes ahead of the others to get his prize a second before his friend—even me! Don't ask me why. It doesn't make sense, but that's how it is.

And now for my story.

\*   \*   \*

One night they gave out a fairly expensive prize in Masmidim: a small radio-controlled car. Usually, they'd give out a small toy that could be bought in a dollar store or a bag of candy. This time, the owner of the toy store had donated the car as a prize for all boys who had attended Masmidim for two whole months in a row.

If everyone raced to get a bag of candy, you can imagine how they raced for the car.

I joined the melee, just like everyone else. Since I'm a fairly strong boy, I was one of the first to stick out my hand and get the prize.

The attack lasted five long minutes, leaving the group leader with two empty hands and one disappointed boy—Yehoshua.

"What about my prize?" he asked.

"I don't know. I gave out forty-three cars to forty-three children. Look at me." He spread his arms wide. "I don't have a single car left."

"How can that be?" Yehoshua started crying.

"Someone must have taken two," the leader declared.

A heavy silence fell on the group. At that moment, the group leader was actually accusing one of us of stealing a second car.

"Here," I said to Yehoshua. "Take mine."

As if that wasn't enough, the group leader looked at me sharply and said, "Wait a minute. Now I remember. You came twice. Yes, you took two cars. I'm certain of it."

Silence filled the room. All the boys stared at me.

"For a minute I thought he was being generous," a boy named Daniel said. "Now it turns out that he was trying to grab two cars, but it didn't work."

"That's not true!" I shouted. "I…I…"

"Rafael, did you take one car or two?" the group leader asked.

"I took two," I said, "but I gave one of them to—"

"Yehoshua," said the group leader. "But that was only after we found out that one car was missing." He sighed. "Rafael, I'm very disappointed in you. Such behavior isn't like you at all."

I started to cry. Right then the toy-store owner walked into the room. He'd donated the cars, and now he wanted to see them being distributed to the boys.

As soon as he walked in, he noticed that something was wrong. "What happened?" he asked.

"It's not important," said the group leader, who didn't want to embarrass me in front of the store owner.

For some reason, the guest turned to look straight at me, maybe because he felt I was at the center of things. "I see that you don't have a car," he said.

Silence.

"I gave mine—" I began.

You couldn't miss hearing the snickers.

"That's why I came," the toy-store owner said. "My worker noticed that eight cars were left in the box of fifty, so I realized right away that I must have given you only forty-two."

The boys looked at him in shock and disbelief, as did the group leader. I was confused, too.

The group leader cleared his throat. He didn't know what to do. Finally, he decided that he had to tell the store owner the truth.

"I think you might be making a mistake," he said to the other man. "We had forty-three cars here. One boy took two by mistake, but now he returned one of the cars."

"Who took two?" the store owner asked.

Everyone remained silent. They didn't want to tattle. But I decided that I had nothing to hide.

"It was me. I took two cars!"

"So where is your car?"

"I gave it to Yehoshua, because he was last and he didn't get a car."

"Okay, but where is the second car?"

"You mean the first car I took? I gave that to my brother Avi. He went home already."

\*   \*   \*

I guess now's the time to tell you about my brother Avi.

Avi is a year older than I am, but whoever sees us together and doesn't know us would never guess.

Avi isn't well. He was born with a lot of serious medical problems, and he's very short and weak.

Avi and I are really good friends, and even though I'm taller and stronger than he is, I show him respect, because he's my older brother. I also help him and defend him when it's necessary. And guess what? It's often necessary. Kids tend to act in ways that are hard to understand toward those who are weaker than they are or have special needs. When that happens, even if I have to fight and suffer, I do it without thinking twice—certainly when it comes to Avi.

And that's exactly what happened when they gave out the cars. Avi, like every boy, wanted to get a car and as fast as possible. That's why I made sure to squeeze in up front to be one of the first. When I got a car, I gave it to Avi. Only after that did I squeeze in a second time to get a car for myself.

If you suspected me of taking two cars for myself (admit it—you did, didn't you?), now you have the explanation of why I took two prizes. And if you understood it, the group leader and the other kids certainly did, too. I mean, they know Avi. He was there that day, and everyone saw that he'd already gone home.

I saw the group leader whisper something to the store owner. Without hearing a word, I knew that he was telling him about Avi and explaining what had happened.

The store owner's eyes grew wide with surprise. His looked at me, and I saw in his eyes pain, astonishment, and great admiration. He asked to speak.

"I understand that you made sure your younger brother got his car first," the store owner said.

"Older," I said. "He looks little, but he's older than I am by a year."

"And then you took a car for yourself."

I nodded.

"Why did you give it to Yehoshua?"

"Because he didn't have one."

"But then you'd be left without a car."

"Yes, but he was very upset about it," I said. "He even…cried."

The store owner gave me a long look. "Listen," he said, "it was worth it for me to donate those cars just to meet a boy like you. I've been running my toy store for years, and I've met many boys. There are good boys, mischievous boys, boys with a good heart, and those who need to work on their *middos*. But I have never before met a boy with such outstanding *middos* as you.

"Boys," he said to the group, "I have a story I want to tell you."

We all know the store owner, Mr. Green. He's a very busy man and a little impatient. We never thought he'd take the time to tell a story to children. But he did. And this is the story he told.

\*    \*    \*

The story takes place over forty years ago (the store owner began). Pinchas, the *gabbai* of our shul, was in charge of the matzah baking every year.

Behind the shul was a large room with an oven inside. That's where the matzah baking took place. About ten men from the shul worked hard to bake the matzos, with Pinchas the *gabbai* supervising them. He was the one who spent the previous two weeks preparing everything. He'd clean the oven, buy the rollers, obtain the flour, get the *mayim shelanu*, cover the tables, and prepare the room for baking matzos. It was unbelievably hard work. And, of course, he was the driving force during the baking itself and worked twice as hard as anyone else in the *chaburah*.

Usually when there is a *chaburah*, all the matzos are divided up among the members. But there were a lot of hangers-on in this *chaburah*. Everyone knew Pinchas, and they all wanted "only" three matzos for the Seder.

People don't know how long it takes to make matzos by hand. If there were only three or four people like this, it wouldn't be a problem. But some fifty people made their way to this makeshift bakery, all of them wanting "only" three matzos. In the end, each baker would be left with maybe nine or ten matzos at the most, with all the rest given out to "friends and relatives."

*   *   *

One year—a year I remember very well—a boy came to the doorway. He wasn't just any boy, but the son of the Bobover Rebbe.

Of course, Pinchas ran to give him three matzos in honor of the Rebbe.

"My father asks for six matzos," the boy said.

Though Pinchas wasn't a Bobover chassid, he admired and respected the Rebbe. But this year many more people came to get matzos than in previous years, and the amount of matzos taken home by the *chaburah* members would be minimal.

"Look," he said, "tell your father, the Rebbe, that we don't have enough matzos this year, so we can give only three to each person."

But the boy insisted. "My father told me to bring six matzos, and I'm not going back to him with three."

Several people in the group began grumbling, but Pinchas signaled them to stop.

"If this is the Rebbe's wish, we will fulfill it. However, please tell your father what I said. Okay?"

The boy agreed and left with six matzos.

The hours flew by, the matzah baking ended, and the *chaburah* members divided up the matzos. This time, each person barely got four. They left feeling pretty angry about the fact that the rest of the shul members came and took matzos as if they had it coming to them. But their greatest anger was directed at the Rebbe's request for six matzos. It seemed exaggerated to them, and if we weren't talking about a distinguished tzaddik, they would have let themselves say what they were thinking.

As if that wasn't enough, on the way out, one of the packages dropped from the hands of its owner, a member of the *chaburah*, and when it was picked up, he found that all the matzos had broken.

The man was very upset, but Pinchas calmed him down by saying that he'd kept one box in reserve. He ran inside and brought the man a box with three whole matzos.

Everyone congratulated Pinchas for planning ahead for such an eventuality, and all the members of the group went home somewhat satisfied that at least everyone had gotten a minimum of three matzos but somewhat disgruntled at having baked hundreds of matzos and taking home only four. But they were used to it already.

Pinchas didn't leave along with the rest. They assumed he was putting the bakery in order before closing it up for Pesach. But Pinchas stayed back for a different reason.

The package he had given the man whose matzos had broken was not a reserve package at all. It was his own package. He didn't want anyone to realize it, so he stayed behind and only left when everyone had gone.

When Pinchas returned home empty-handed, his family was not surprised. They knew their father and were used to the fact that when all was said and done, they almost never ate the matzos that were baked in the *chaburah* he organized.

Usually what would happen is that he would bring one package home, and then, after davening, only minutes before the Seder, someone or other would always knock on the door saying he had "forgotten" to take his matzos because he hadn't had time. Or an angry shul member would come saying he'd sent his son, but they hadn't given him any. Pinchas would give away his package and say to his family, "This mitzvah is worth a lot more than the mitzvah of eating matzos specially baked in the afternoon just before the Seder." He would be especially joyous at the Seder with store-bought matzos.

The fact that this time he hadn't even brought home a box wasn't any big news. Anyway, the family hardly ever got to taste those matzos, so what was new?

To spare the shul members from a wasted trip to his house, he made an announcement after davening.

"This year there are no reserve matzos," he told everyone. "There's no point in coming to my house, because I don't have any matzos to give."

And that's what happened. That year, unlike all the other years, not a single person came to his house after davening to ask for matzos.

*   *   *

The family crowded excitedly around the Seder table. The Seder plate was prepared, and the matzos (store-bought) were waiting for *Kadesh*.

Right then, they heard knocks on the door.

Someone ran to open it, and who do you think stood there?

The boy who had showed up at the matzah baking earlier that day — the son of the Bobover Rebbe.

In his hand was a box of hand matzos, one of the two he had taken that afternoon.

What was going on?

"My father asked me to take six matzos this

afternoon, three for him and three to save for you. He'd heard that often you were left without a single matzah from the *chaburah*, so he asked me to insist that you give me double. Only now, when everyone has started their Seder, did he send me. He wanted to be certain that no one would come and take from you what is rightfully yours."

Out of all the people, only the Bobover Rebbe thought about the matzos of Pinchas the *gabbai*, and found a clever way to make sure he would have at least three matzos from the *chaburah* for his Seder.

\* \* \*

The toy-store owner ended his story, looked at all of us, and said, "I'm sure you all have a good idea why I remembered this story, which took place some forty years ago, now. This boy, Rafael, combines the kindness of Pinchas with the caring of the Bobover Rebbe. He made sure to take a car for his brother Avi, and then, when there weren't enough cars to go around, he didn't hesitate to give his own car to Yehoshua. This behavior combines the two good *middos* of two people who are no longer with us, but who were known for their nobility of soul.

"We didn't understand at first what was behind

the request of the Bobover Rebbe. That's because an ordinary person doesn't think along those lines. He wouldn't dream that the Rebbe's request was made not for himself but for Pinchas the *gabbai*.

"In the same way, you didn't dream that Rafael would give away his car out of the goodness of his heart. You were certain that he was keeping two for himself. It never occurred to you that he'd given the first to his brother."

The story made a big impact on the boys, and they felt bad for wrongly suspecting me. The group leader said, "I want to ask Rafael to forgive me for suspecting him."

All the boys came over to me and also apologized.

"I almost forgot that I came here to give you the missing prize," the store owner said. "Right after I left the store, I went back inside. I said to myself that if one car was missing, maybe two were missing. To be on the safe side, I took an extra car. I'm sure all of you will agree with my decision to give Rafael two cars. He deserves it, doesn't he?"

All the boys agreed enthusiastically, and the store owner gave me the double prize.

He said to me, "If you ever need anything, just step into my store."

"Mr. Green," I said to him, "you didn't tell us how you knew about the story you just told us."

"You're right," he said. "Which reminds me. I wanted to ask you all a favor, and this will give you your answer. Boys, I made a donation to your Masmidim program today, and I hope to give more to this wonderful program. Just promise me that when you daven and when you learn, you will keep in mind that it should be a merit for Shraga ben Pinchas. Yes, I am the son of Pinchas the *gabbai*."

# Glossary

The following glossary provides a partial explanation of some of the Hebrew, Yiddish, and Aramaic words and phrases used in this book. The spellings and explanations reflect the way the specific word is used herein. Often, there are alternate spellings and meanings for the words.

Abba: Father

*afikoman*: The middle of three matzos at the Seder table, customarily broken in half and hidden for children to find

*alter bachur* (Y.): The oldest boy in the yeshivah

*avrech*: Married man who learns Torah most of the day

*avrech chashuv*: A married Torah scholar

*bachur* (pl. *bachurim*): Yeshivah student

bar mitzvah: A Jewish boy of thirteen, the age at which he accepts religious obligations; the celebration marking the occasion

*bashert* (Y.): Predestined spouse

*b'chavrusa*: To study together

*beis medrash* (pl. *batei medrash*): Study hall

*bentch gomel* (Y.): To recite the special prayer after being saved from a dangerous situation

*ben Torah*: Lit., "son of the Torah." One who loves Torah and devotes his life to Torah

*bubby*: (Y.) Grandmother

*chaburah* (pl. *chaburos*): Group

*chasan*: Bridegroom

*chavrusa* (pl. *chavrusos*): Study partner

*Chazal*: Acronym for "*chachameinu zichronam livrachah*—our Sages, of blessed memory"; the Sages of the Talmud

*cherem* (Y.): Decree of exclusion from the community

*chinuch*: Education

chutzpah, chutzpadik (Y.): Act fresh

daven(ing) (Y.): Pray

*frum* (Y.): Religious

*gabbai*: Sexton of a shul

*gadol hador* (pl. *gedolei hador*): Great Torah scholar of the generation

*geshmak* (Y.): Sweet; delicious

*hasmadah*: Diligence

*Kadesh*: The Kiddush made over wine that begins the Seder

*Karpas*: Greens dipped in salt water at the Seder

*kittel*: White garment worn over a suit at the Seder

*lamdanim*: Torah scholars

*lashon hara*: a remark that belittles or harms another person; gossip

*l'chaim*: small celebration for immediate family and close friends made when a couple decides to get engaged

*masechtos*: Tractates of the Talmud

Masmidim: Lit., those who learn Torah every possible minute; an after-school program where boys learn Torah

*mayim shelanu*: Water drawn the previous night used for baking matzos

*meforshim*: commentators

*middah* (pl. *middos*): Character trait

*minhag*: Custom

*nachas*: Pleasure; joy

*nu* (Y.): Well; so

*perek*: Chapter

Pesach: Passover

*potch* (*potches*): Spanking

*rabbeim*: Torah scholars who staff a yeshivah

*Rashi*: Acronym for Rabbi Shlomo Yitzchaki, the foremost commentator on Talmud and Chumash

*rav*: Rabbi

*rechilus*: Gossip

*roshei yeshivah*: Deans of a yeshivah

*sefer*: Torah-related publication

*shadchan gelt*: Money given to one who makes, or helps to make, a *shidduch*

*shidduch*: Marital match

*shlita*: Acronym for *"sheyichyeh l'orech yamim tovim aruchim"* added to the name of a Torah scholar of renown as a blessing that live many long and good days

shul: Synagogue

*Shulchan Orech*: The Seder meal

*siyatta diShmaya*: Heavenly help

*sugya*: Talmudic discussion

*talmid chacham*: A Torah scholar

*talmidim*: Students

*Tehillim*: The book of Psalms

*Tosafos*: Medieval commentaries on the Talmud

*tzaddeikes*: A pious woman or girl

tzaddik: A pious man or boy

*Tzafun*: At the Seder, finding the *afikoman* and eating it

*Urchatz*: Ritual washing of the hands at the Seder

*vort*: Celebration of an engagement

*Yachatz*: Breaking the middle matzah at the Seder

*zivug hagun*: Worthy marriage partner

ztz"l: Acronym for "*zecher tzaddik livrachah*—may the memory of this tzaddik be for blessing," added to the name of a deceased righteous individual, usually a Torah sage